CW00832631

God's Healing Word

Felicity Corbin-Wheeler

BookPublishingWorld

A BookPublishingWorld Book

Copyright © BookPublishingWorld 2006

Text Copyright © Felicity Corbin Wheeler 2006

Cover design by James Fitt ©

Main Cover Photograph of Apricot tree by Peter Firus
www.photos.flagstaffotos.com

Printed in Great Britain

ISBN: 1-905553-08-0

The information in this book, given without prejudice, healed the author. It is biblically based. However God lays choices before us and it is up to each individual to accept or reject biblical teaching. The author cannot accept responsibility for readers' decisions, which by law must be taken together with the advice of their medical and nutritional advisors. No responsibility is attributable to the author, except to recommend God's healing word.

God's Healing Word

Introduction

God says: "My people are destroyed from lack of knowledge"
Hosea 4:6

This book is all about healing. I pray that it will heal YOU!

We are living in a sick world, fearful of cancer, heart disease, MRSA, bird flu, arthritis, diabetes, obesity, digestive and respiratory difficulties and countless other health problems. Christians are as sick as the rest of society. We know God can and does heal miraculously, but many of us are still sick. Why?
Why do good, kind people get sick and die before their time?

If you really want to know how to heal, or to stay well and keep well, read on...

The biblically based knowledge contained in this book healed me from terminal pancreatic cancer in the autumn of 2003.

It was the information we desperately needed when our dearly loved 18 year old daughter Melanie had cancer sixteen years earlier. She died after enduring two years of surgery, chemotherapy and radiation. The "best" of treatment from the British cancer establishment. She and I knew there must be a better way, and I promised her I would spend the rest of my life trying to find it.

Ever since her death I had searched the world for a real cure to cancer, and a way to prevent cancer in the first place. I was trained as a researcher in the Houses of Parliament and I have done my search diligently. But it was only when I was diagnosed with a no hope, no treatment cancer myself that I found the answer.

I went to my London church and a woman pastor prayed for me most powerfully. She also told me about God's health directives. They healed me. The websites and books she told me about were a revelation.

What I learned about cancer astonished me.
I learned that it is a healing process that has gone wrong in the body, because our immune systems are damaged by our lifestyles and the food we eat.
I learned that cancer is caused by the lack of certain vital enzymes in the body, which are depleted still further when we eat animal protein.
I learned that all degenerative disease, including cancer, can be healed once we start to give the body the living enzymes it needs. And the answer was in God's Word.

God has given us His diet and the manual for life in His Word in the Bible. If we are disobedient we suffer. His instructions are clear. Our lives are blessed or cursed, according to whether we are obedient to Him. I believed, I became obedient to his laws, and I was completely healed. The answer is given in the Word of God, the Bible. We just do not read it, and if we do, all too often we do not understand it.

As Hosea says, "we are destroyed from lack of knowledge."

When we receive blessings from God, we must pass them on to others, and He has put it on my heart to write this book for you, if you are seeking truth and healing.

Despite huge government investment, orthodox medicine has simply not provided an answer to degenerative disease. Cancer, heart disease, asthma, osteoporosis, digestive disease, arthritis and diabetes are all on the increase and we are getting sicker earlier. Children and even babies develop cancer, and diabetes is escalating among teenagers.

With governments unable to fund decent health care for everyone, and our hospitals rife with disease, it is time for us to become responsible for our own health. We must learn how to prevent disease as well as how to cure it.

Pancreatic cancer is probably the most deadly and fastest killing. I was given a few weeks to live. The radiologist who has scanned me since the healing looked at the original scans and said that the tumour was so bad that actually I would have only survived three weeks!

The scans now show the tumour reduced to a mere scar, which is exactly how the essence of living enzymes is supposed to work. I am alive and well, completely out of pain and able to witness around the world. God has given me a gracious life extension and I start each day by thanking God and asking Him what He would have me do with this precious gift.

It is my huge privilege and blessing to be able to answer hundreds of people who have heard about the healing, and phone, e mail and write from all over the world. I can encourage them and pray with them over the phone, but there are many more who need to be reached. I pray that this book will be a life-saver for many, and reach the younger generation <u>before</u> they succumb to illness.

Sometimes the Bible stops us in our tracks. I found our family name in there!

Because we are a Channel Island family, we have a French name "Corbin". Jesus tells us in Mark 7:11 that the Hebrew word "Corban" means "a gift devoted to God."

Melanie Corbin was a gift devoted to God. I dedicated all my children to God, but because of pollution and lifestyle her life was tragically cut short. Her loss has been devastating to our family, but she had an extraordinary encounter with an angel when she was diagnosed alone in London and she died with incredible peace and grace. She knew God and she simply went back home to Him sooner than any of us expected. Her angel told her what was to happen, and led her home.

But she longed to find a cure not only for herself but for others. Through her, my life became devoted to God and His Healing Word. She is the inspiration for this book, which can heal us on earth, and bring us the greatest healing of all, salvation.

Let´s start with a prayer.

Heavenly Father,

You are the Great Healer,

and your Word is a Healing Word.

Jesus, your Son, healed as He walked the earth,

and through His Holy Spirit, He still heals us today.

I commit this book into Your hands, to write through my hands.

Dear Lord, open hearts and minds to your Word,

and inspire me to inspire others,

in Jesus' all powerful, healing name.

Amen

Chapter One

Melanie´s story

"Mum, I´ve something to tell you."

Melanie Joy, my lovely, sunny daughter, newly an undergraduate at Kings College, London University, had just arrived in my London hotel room overlooking the Thames and Tower Bridge, on her 18th birthday.

"Mum - I´ve got cancer."

With that, she dashed for the bathroom and was very, very, ill for the next nine hours.

Her nineteen year old boyfriend Gary, so good looking and usually so confident, looked at me in despair. Gary is Greek and suddenly looked very young.

"We´ve come straight from the hospital. Mel´s just had her first chemotherapy" he said, brokenly, twisting his hands. His dark eyes were filled with anguish.

I had seen Melanie for lunch in London only four days before and she had seemed perfectly well and happy, long blonde hair swinging. I had thought how stunning she was, how brave, coping well in London after only a month away from home in Jersey.

We had a "special treat" lunch together at the Savoy Hotel, next to her university in Somerset House. And we arranged to have dinner on her birthday in four days time, the night I arrived back from Hong Kong.

Feeling so happy that she was settling down well, and my other daughter nursing and my son doing well at school in Jersey, I got on the plane that afternoon to take part in the Algarve Exhibition in

Hong Kong. For many years my husband Alan and I had owned a small holiday home in the Algarve, overlooking the beach.

I now had my own marketing company, selling similar villas, both large and small, on a beautiful Algarve estate by the sea and golf course. I worked on a flat 5% commission. I paid all my own advertising expenses and chose my own markets. I invested all my commissions into upgrading our little house. We had originally paid £14,000 and these homes are now reaching £500,000. God is not making more land right there!

I had also just completed two years as Lady Captain of the Royal Jersey golf club and was looking forward to a break. Happily, my husband was visiting a branch of his firm's office in Hong Kong so we made a four day celebration holiday together.

So, having worked a thirteen hour day for four days at the Algarve Exhibition, and jet-lagged from the return flight, I slept most of the day in the Tower Hotel in London, waiting for Melanie and her handsome Greek boyfriend to join me for the birthday dinner. My husband had flown straight through to Jersey for work the next morning.

I put my arms round Melanie as she convulsed again and again over the basin, I could feel the icy sweat soaking her long blonde hair. I held her hair back and smoothed it out of the way, tied it in a lose plait, as I had done when she first went to school. Again and again, as her body retched, my heart broke and my mind raced.

How had my lovely girl got cancer? Would she survive? No one in our immediate family had had cancer, my parents were still alive and well in their 80's and my husband parents, now gone, had not had cancer.

Gary told me Melanie had been diagnosed with Hodgkin's Disease, a cancer of the lymph glands. The oncologist at King's College Hospital, her university hospital, said that there was an 85% chance of cure. They had warned him that she might be very sick from the chemotherapy, that was perfectly normal….

But this situation continued for hour after hour and she was on the point of collapse. Had they given her too much chemo? I rang Kings College hospital to find that only the casualty department was open, would I please ring again in the morning.

I rang down to the hotel reception to ask if they had a hotel doctor. They said they would get one. At three in the morning, Gary had gone back to his flat, and Mel was still retching her heart out. An Australian woman doctor in her late twenties arrived and gave her an injection. Eventually Mel fell asleep, exhausted, deathly white, beside me on my hotel bed.

Dr. Jane Reffell talked to me about Hodgkin's and chemotherapy. She was new to London, and she told me to look at natural, alternative healing as well. I shall never forget her compassion as she spent over an hour with me. "Remember the spiritual side of the healing is as important as the physical, with cancer." She said. "Keep her believing for her healing."

The next morning Melanie and I got a taxi down to Kings College Hospital, and saw the woman oncologist. She was warm, in her thirties, and obviously she and Melanie had established a rapport. Melanie had told her she did not want to worry her parents until she was sure of the diagnosis. I was torn apart to think of her courage.

But the bad news was that Melanie's cancer was already at stage 4B.
That meant it has spread badly through her body.

Melanie was too ill to continue with university. I rang a friend of mine who had survived this particular cancer a few years earlier. She advised Melanie to come home to rest; the chemo was going to be very hard as she had reacted so badly to the first course. Celia had had a dreadful time with her chemo, and said that it could be given in Jersey which obviated the exhausting travelling to and fro when feeling so nauseous.

I rang my husband in his office, and broke the news. I remember tears streaming down my face in the telephone box in the hotel as I spoke to him. Melanie was asleep in the bedroom upstairs. Tears were running down his face in the office in Jersey. I could hear them in his voice.

That afternoon, Mel's 18th birthday, we flew back to Jersey. It was agreed that she would have the remaining five chemotherapy sessions either in London or in the Jersey hospital, at the directive of her London oncologist. She would then have radiotherapy at St. Thomas' Hospital in London.

Melanie had to have a wheelchair to the plane, and seeing her being lifted on to the plane was heartbreaking. I hid the tears as she was lowered into the seat beside me. One of the ambulance men, not much older than her, was pretty upset, too.

The effect on her father, sister and brother and her grandparents was shocking. We were a very close, loving family. Only six months previously, our fourteen year old son had had to have his appendix out, and a week later, as the surgeon took his stitches out, he asked me to have a word with him in his consulting room.

"Nothing to worry about", he said, "but I must tell you that Giles had a carcinoid tumour in his appendix. It's all gone, it was encapsulated, but I am duty bound to tell you what I found."

I looked at him in shock. Previously I had worked for an eminent top cancer surgeon in London, during the Parliamentary recesses, and I was staggered.

"Are you all right?" the surgeon asked me, as Giles walked back into the room, putting his school blazer back on. So young. Too young.

Not wanting to frighten Giles, I thanked the surgeon and we drove home. He without a care in the world, operation over, but with an icy heaviness in my heart.

When we got home I quietly rang Harvey White at the Royal Marsden in London and told him what had happened. His response was immediate and concerned.

"Felicity, bring him over to me next week and we'll give him a complete check up."

The Jersey doctor and hospital were resistant to letting the histology – the bright yellow carcinoid tumour encapsulated in a transparent slide, out of their hands, but I insisted. I even had to leave the doctor's practice. But I got the slide. I began to feel distrust at the arrogance and high handed manner that affects too many of the medical establishment.

We flew to London the next week and Giles, at fourteen, had to undergo a full body scan and dozens of tests. A frightening experience for a boy. He was suddenly surrounded by nuclear warning signs and white coated experts. I read a whole Jack Higgins book that day, and afterward could not recall a word I had read.

At the end of it all, they found that the carcinoid had not spread, but that Giles has a chronic liver disease called Gilbert's, after the French specialist who had first researched it. This is not life threatening, but means that his liver would always be compromised and that he should avoid physical stress, which overloads the liver.

The doctors in Jersey had completely omitted to find this, but when Harvey White's report was relayed to our general practitioner there, he rang me urgently to warn Giles not to run the cross country at school. Too late! Giles had already run!

To find that Melanie now had full blown cancer so soon after her brother's scare seemed to me more than a co-incidence. I discovered other girls at Melanie's school had cancer. A boy at Giles'school also had cancer at the same time.

I spoke with a cancer epidemiologist with world wide experience of cancer. She wondered if the nuclear station across the water in France at Cap de la Hague had anything to do with it. I did local research through an environmental group called Concern. It seemed that there were indeed groups called "clusters" of childhood cancers found near such nuclear processing stations. There was also danger from radon found in granite.

I had our granite farmhouse checked out for radon. Nothing untoward. I then had the water checked out. The water in our three hundred year old farmhouse well turned out to contain a high rate of toxins. They had been sprayed on the crops and eventually seeped into the 40 foot deep level of the well.

I very much wanted to leave Jersey and settle in Portugal, to give the children a cleaner environment. Two sick children out of three were odds I did not like.

In between supporting Mel through her monthly chemo sessions in London and Jersey I built up my business in Portugal and tried to persuade my husband to move. All I wanted was healthy children. I could not get out of Jersey fast enough. But he wanted to stay in Jersey where he had built up a stock broking office. It had grown to a hundred employees and he had an office in Guernsey, too. Understandably he did not want to move.

Melanie was having a dreadful time with the chemotherapy. She was desperately ill every month; her body was just not strong enough to take the toxic treatments. The tumours seemed to shrink each time, and then return. It was what they call an aggressive cancer. Six months later she went to London for the radiotherapy.

We were able to stay in the London home of one of my oldest friends, Anne, and her children. Her own husband had died of cancer in his thirties. Independent to the ultimate degree, Melanie refused to let me have a taxi and go with her to St. Thomas's Hospital every day. She insisted on doing it all alone on public transport. It was heartbreaking.

Eventually she asked that her best friend from Jersey come and stay in Anne's house in London. It had been arranged months earlier that Anne and her children were to holiday in our villa in Portugal at that time, and Melanie begged me to go with them. She said she would feel much better if she lived a normal life without being "mothered".

I was starting to learn how painful motherhood could really be! Childbirth was nothing to what I was feeling now. I had heard it said in the pre natal classes by a wise midwife called Betty Parsons that the first cutting of the umbilical chord is not the painful one. I was now learning what she had meant!

Six weeks after the radiation the cancer had come back. She was now in great danger. The woman oncologist in London moved Melanie to the care of her own Professor at the Royal Marsden in Sutton. "If anyone can save Mel, he will", she said. "He's the best in the world."

To be near Mel, I slept in a motel near the Royal Marsden in Sutton, where we met for the first time this Professor of Oncology.

Melanie underwent another three months of chemotherapy. She was getting weaker with each session and she was in a ward with five other women most of who smoked. The sister said "well they're going to die anyway so they might as well indulge themselves."

I got Melanie into a room on her own.

I kept thinking there had to be a better way. I went to buy special fruit and other little presents for her every day. And in a bookshop in Sutton I found a book on the Gerson Therapy. This was a cancer therapy founded by a German, Dr. Max Gerson, based on detoxing the body and building up the immune system with fresh juices. His clinic was based in Mexico because the cancer establishment vigorously condemned any natural treatments for cancer. Consensus medicine consisted of cutting, burning and poisoning the cancer. They discounted the theory that the body could heal itself if given the right conditions.

But Gerson's theory made sense to me, particularly as Melanie was not getting better with the toxic chemotherapy. She was dying before my eyes. I suggested we went to Mexico to the Gerson Clinic.

But Melanie was a scientist and she trusted science to save her. She just could not believe that it would not work. The white coats and authoritative manner of the cancer establishment are hard to challenge, especially when one is feeling so ill.

Then one October morning she was in crisis. I arrived early morning as usual, to find her gasping for breath. One of her lungs collapsed. She could hardly breathe and was in great pain. Despite her courage, there was real fear in her eyes. I ran into the corridor to get help.

That was the first time we went to the High Dependency Unit, in other words, intensive care. As Mel's life was now in the balance, the hospital allowed me to sleep in a visitor's room, next door. It was Christmas, and as the Salvation Army played carols in the grounds below, I held Mel's hand as she was given a bone marrow transplant.

It was the last hope, and it was harrowing. It burned Mel's digestive system from the mouth all the way down. It was hell on earth. But she never once complained. She just cried out "Oh Mum" in her sleep and I would get up off the folding "zed" hospital bed and hold her hands. She had a lot of morphine but it did not stop the pain. My heart broke as I knelt beside her bed, begging God to save her.

There were two chaplains who visited, a good looking young Roman Catholic, who was dressed from head to toe in black.
"Keep him out of my room", Mel said. "He looks like funerals!"
The other was a Methodist, a homely middle aged man in a sports jacket. She enjoyed his visits.

We also went up to the chapel when she was in between treatments. It had a peaceful atmosphere and lots of candles and notes left asking for prayers for patients. They were so poignant to read, but we read them, and prayed for these faceless names. Many of them were small children. Before I lived in at the Marsden I had no idea that some babies are born with cancer.

Despite the last hope chemotherapy, which only gave a one in three chance of cure, Mel relapsed again immediately. The doctors had told me before Christmas that they did not think she was going to survive. But she had tried so hard to live.

I rang my husband and Mel's boyfriend in Jersey. We were going to need their support, physically and emotionally, on the flight home. But the doctor who was to sign the release would not come to tell Mel and results of the last tests. He promised to come, but just did not turn up. We all sat waiting in Mel's room.

In the end I went to his office where I found he was packing his briefcase for a lecture visit to America. I said to him with courage born of desperation. "You really cannot just fly off to America without telling Mel. The nurses are not allowed to do it, its up to you, they say, and we want to get her home as soon as we can."

He came. He told us.

I asked if they could put me out and give Mel one of my lungs. Any mother would. The answer was no. Within an hour we were driving to Gatwick for the last time. Attempts at cheerfulness fell silent. We just drove and watched the lights go by on the motorway and the rain fall like tears on the windscreen.

Arriving back at home, Mel went to her own comfy little bedroom at last. She asked to be left alone, and locked the door. Alan and I had to tell Camilla and Giles the bad news - the treatments had failed and Mel did not have long to live. Their faces were terrible to watch. Shock, disbelief, and then wrenching grief and anger. We sat round the kitchen table and held hands. The tears ran down our faces unashamedly. I knew whatever we had been through, whatever she had suffered physically and emotionally, the worst was still to come.

The next morning early I rang a neighbour who I knew was a Hospice sister. Within an hour Sheila was sitting with us, armed with practical comforts, understanding and compassion.

Mel was losing her sight because her blood was so depleted. I rang the pathologists in Jersey for a transfusion. We were met with hostility. I just could not believe what I was hearing from the head pathologist, now retired.

However, that night another pathologist at the Jersey hospital, now dead so he cannot be disciplined, broke all the rules. He arrived at our house, looking tired, with a drip stand and a packet of blood. He had actually drawn off his own blood as he and Melanie both belonged to the same blood group.

The love and sheer self sacrifice was a blessing in the face of so much arrogance we had faced from the medical establishment. His boss, who knew Melanie and me personally and was supposed to be a friend, had actually said "there are people much sicker than Melanie, you know". As she died later that week, I could hardly believe that, and told him so.

But at least she could see for her few remaining days, thanks to the compassionate assistant pathologist. When he died a few years later I wrote a letter telling his wife of his kindness.

Too many doctors are arrogant and ignorant. When Melanie had been made so ill by the second chemotherapy, I had asked the "world famous oncologist" if I could take Melanie to America to try the Gerson diet, based on juices. He turned on me and said,
"Mrs. Corbin, if you think lettuce leaves will cure your daughter, take her away and stop wasting my time".

Mel looked at me in horror. We were chastened, intimidated into submission, and Mel died three months later from the bone marrow transplant. There is an interesting end note to the story. This eminent man committed suicide six months later. He had just rubbished the natural Bristol Cancer Centre on BBC TV. Maybe he began to wonder if he was wrong?

Melanie had been told at Christmas when she had the bone marrow transplant that if it did not work she would be dead by Easter. Three days before she died she went to the dentist and managed to climb the stairs to his first floor surgery. That night she went out for dinner with her faithful Gary. She wrapped her poor smooth head in one of my black chiffon scarves, wore a very smart black dress and held her head up high. The next day she went to her little bed for the last time. Her room was filled with friends and flowers and cards.

On Maundy Thursday, the day before Good Friday, our lovely girl, so weak and frail, succumbed to one last chest infection. This time she refused antibiotics. She did not want to fight any more.

Our doctor came in every day and gave her painkillers. Her breathing grew more and more laboured and we sat beside her bed all day and all night. My poor husband Alan could not believe she would die. Sheila of the Hospice tells me this is so often the reaction of fathers. The last day her godfather Rob Riley who was then a Commander in the Fleet Air Arm, and a Christian, flew a Navy training plane over to Jersey for a few precious hours.

The last thing I said to her was we all loved her so much and she was going to Jesus. We would all be following her. The morphine then took over and she spent one last night laboriously drawing in ever shallower breaths, with us sitting vigil beside her. Camilla and I took the first watch, and around four in the morning the boys took over, her father, seventeen year old brother and the ever faithful boyfriend Gary.

At half past nine in the morning, when the young ones had gone to shower and change, and I had gone to get some juice and fruit for the family, she sat up, expectantly. She was alone with Alan. She looked at him and then sighed one last deep sigh and fell back on the pillows and died with complete grace. I heard him cry out. He came into the kitchen and grabbed my hand.

"Come quickly", he called "I think she's gone…he said with tears pouring down his face. We went into her room hand in hand and there she was, gone to be with the Lord.

Melanie had told me an amazing story when she was first diagnosed. She told me that when she had had the biopsy in London, she was sitting up in bed, wide awake, when an angel appeared on her bed and told her what was going to happen.

"Oh Mel", I said "surely it was a doctor or a nurse dressed in white?"

"Mum" she said, with the despairing tone of voice only teenagers adopt to their parents when they are being particularly thick, "don't you think that I would know the difference. This was huge and had wings!"

To my great shame, at the time I just did not believe her. I had never seen an angel, so I could not imagine that she had. But the grace and dignity with which she died was her witness. What an example to all of us. Her angel was real, and of course they are biblical. Maybe her angel came to fetch her as she left us.

As is traditional in Jersey, Mel's body was prepared, dressed and returned to rest at home. Her casket lay at the foot of our bed, just as the crib had done when she was a baby. It felt so strange to see her life from beginning to end. It is so unnatural, and I still weep as I watch other, unknown, mothers and fathers mourning their dead children on the news. I cannot help it. The compassion just pours out of my eyes.

Her service could not be held until after Easter, which allowed us more time to just be with her and hold her and look for one last time at her beautiful face, her hands, even her feet. I counted every one of her eyelashes, and her eyebrows, which had started to grow again. I held her hands, which they had crossed, and which were stiff but still so slim and beautiful.

Her thanksgiving service was packed with friends of all ages. In the church where she and her sister had lit the candles for each child during the Christingle service two years previously, she was now leading the way from darkness to light through her service. Her graduation service. Many came to the Lord through her witness.

Her friend Sarah played the oboe. Others sang in the choir. Her teachers were there. It was the Easter holidays.

Jesus had risen, now we are waiting for the final day when all believers in Jesus will rise together. That is the promise of Jesus himself. Melanie is in our future as well as our past. The stars are always there, even when hidden by clouds. For us, she is always just a smile away. And we are moving towards her.

Chapter Two

Felicity´s story

"A voice is heard in Ramah,
Mourning and great weeping,
Rachel weeping for her children
And refusing to be comforted,
Because her children are no more." Jeremiah 31:15

The grace and peace of Melanie´s death, her lovely smile, was life changing to all who witnessed it.

Families who lose children tragically either grow very close or are torn apart. I know and have prayed with families who made it through, but there is always a huge battle. Emotions are too raw to bear, or to share. It is just too painful to communicate. When suffering is so intense, it is only through Jesus and his infinite compassion and promise of eternal life, that we can find hope and meaningful words of peace and comfort. If our lives on earth are the end of the story, there is no justice and no sense to life.

As King Solomon, a man who had untold wisdom, power, riches, honour and reputation, says in the beginning of the book of Ecclesiastes, life is "meaningless, meaningless" when viewed from a solely intellectual, worldly perspective. He ends the book with the conclusion "fear God and keep His commandments".

In a world of infinite intelligence, designed by an infinitely intelligent creator, nothing is lost. Moisture from the seas rises and falls as rain which eventually returns to the sea again in rivers. Individual waves merge back into the sea. There is no reincarnation in the body. As Hebrews 9:27 says, *"It is appointed for mortals to die once, and then face judgement."*

Our spirits are released from the earth body we have used for a life span, which gradually decays, dies and returns to earth. What we have done is done, it cannot be changed. We face judgement. The spirit lives on, but where?

The creator is a God of mercy, holiness and justice. Sin has to be paid for. If we die in our sins, we will be punished, and the wages of sin is death. We all sin, so we all deserve death. But Jesus came as God in human form to take sin upon his shoulders and die for us by crucifixion, the cruellest death devised by men. Only by his blood are we saved.

Our need for Jesus is absolute. We do not become Christians to be members of a cosy Sunday morning club, although true Christian fellowship is our greatest comfort on earth. We become Christians to save us from deserved certain hell and eternal damnation, and to experience the joy and peace that passes all human understanding! And when we come into obedience, we start experiencing the extraordinary blessing of God. Healings happen in many ways, and the greatest healing of all is our salvation.

When we understand this truth, we long to pass it on to others who are struggling with the world. Everyone struggles at some time or another. We need to be armed for the struggle!

When Jesus is the greatest influence in a family, that family will survive all attacks, including bereavement, and grow stronger. But unfortunately most of us are not armed spiritually. We think we are secure, but when we come under severe attack from the devil who seeks only to steal, kill and destroy, we do not have the armour of God to overcome satan's wiles. One thing he longs to destroy is marriage, because it is the foundation of the family.

Paul, writing in Ephesians 6:10 explains that we live in spiritual darkness, struggling against the powers of darkness and spiritual forces of evil in the heavenly realms. We need to arm ourselves every day. The first thing we need is to fortify ourselves with the belt of truth, which is the Word of God. The truth, as Jesus said, will always set us free.

Our second piece of armour is the breastplate of righteousness, being "right with God", which we can only do through honesty and true repentance. God only accepts the broken and contrite heart, and welcomes back only His truly repentant sons and daughters.

We also need to cover ourselves with the peace of the Gospel and the readiness to speak it out in our lives and share it with others. This gives us the shield of God, and the helmet of salvation which keeps our thinking right.

So far, the armour has been for our defence, but now God arms us with a sword of the Holy Spirit to use against the enemy, and this sword is the Word of God in the Bible. The "Word" also refers to Jesus. When you speak the Word, the devil flees. Try it! It works! Finally, Paul reminds us we need to pray in the Spirit on all occasions. Only then can we overcome attack and turn it into the victory that Christ died to give us.

However, we as a family were not properly prepared for this huge attack of the enemy, and we were devastated. Although we trusted that Melanie had gone to be with the Lord, we did not at that time know Him ourselves. Our lives were desolate. Our joy had gone. The devil was tearing us apart. He had already stolen, he had already killed and now he set about destroying the heart of the family.

I had spent the last six months alone with Mel in hospital. We had become closer than just mother and daughter. We had become each other's lifeline. I was desperate not to lose touch. The fact I could not lift a phone and talk to her was the hardest. I kept thinking of things I wanted to share with her. I kept seeing girls who looked like her in the street. When they turned round, it was not Melanie. I was finding the grief unbearable.

Our church was not, at that time, Holy Spirit filled. The sparse congregation was elderly and there were no supportive house groups at that time. Our very kind and dear vicar, who we loved, and who had been so faithful, was stone deaf. I longed to communicate with him but the feelings were too painful to share in notes and sign language.

My husband and children found it too painful to return to the church after the lovely thanksgiving service. Soon my tears embarrassed me so much in the church that I stopped going.

Our golfing friends were appalled and embarrassed by the tragedy. They did not know what to say and apart from flowers and cards, they went on with their golf and I simply did not. They probably felt dreadfully sorry for us. That did not help much. Nothing did!

My husband turned to his office. He worked later and later and was exasperated by my grief when he did come home. Because I found no comfort and healing, I could not heal the family. The mother is so important. If she does not know the Lord, the family crumbles.

Our sensitive elder daughter was profoundly hurt and deeply angry that her sister had died, despite her prayers. Because we were reduced to tears whenever we spoke about Mel, she tried not to communicate. She moved into a flat with some girlfriends within six weeks. It was heartbreaking to lose another daughter.

Our son had to concentrate on his forthcoming A levels. He was so full of grief that he had to walk out of the mock exams; but with great courage managed to pass all his subjects and get into a good university to read Politics and Law. I felt a huge sense of relief that he, also, had something new to move on to, and would be concentrating on the challenges of life at university.

My husband and I were left alone in the house. It was so empty and I tried to find a job. The girl who interviewed me was young enough to be another daughter. "Oh yes," she said, "I know your husband very well. We had lunch together yesterday." Ouch. Apparently I needed computer skills to get any kind of a job, and at that time I had never seen a computer! I tried to learn but could not concentrate.

My father died a few months later and on the weekend of his funeral my husband told me that he simply did not want to be married any more. We were both at fault, and I admitted my mistakes which were many, but he was adamant, he wanted to be free. Loving him as I did, I could see he needed his freedom. I just had not got the heart to persevere. We were forgetting that God was also in our marriage covenant and that it could not be broken. Forgiveness is absolute, and salvation is absolute. Both are only possible through Jesus.

So I quietly and sadly went home to my mother. When winter arrived I asked my husband if I could take my mother to live with me in our little house in Portugal. He was only too glad!

My poor mother broke her hip within three days of arriving in Portugal. Many of the pavements are made of cobbles called calçadas, and she fell badly. She was carried back to the villa and taken for an X ray by ambulance. The fracture was very bad, and the doctor told us we would have to go to Lisbon for an operation.

The jolting ambulance took four hours to reach the Red Cross Hospital in Lisbon, and when we arrived the driver left us at the morgue and disappeared! I found a doctor who spoke English, and we were then wheeled to reception. There my mother's credit card was divested of £500 and we were eventually shown to a room on the top floor. The nurses manhandled my mother on to a bed and indicated that I could sleep on the other bed. Memories of the "zed bed" at the Royal Marsden.

My mother had brought with her the telephone number of Ken Robinson, the British Chaplain in Lisbon. Within an hour Ken was visiting us, and we had some prayer. The next day my mother had her operation. She was then eighty eight and had suffered from a weak heart for many years. We knew the operation was going to be a battle, but Graça, a very competent woman cardiologist, resuscitated my mother three times when her heart stopped under the anaesthetic. She was so long in the operating theatre that I went searching for it, and actually watched from plastic screening in the entrance as Luis da Costa, the Portuguese orthopaedic surgeon, did a wonderful job.

Within a week we were back to the Algarve in another ambulance. The countryside looked much prettier on the return journey!

Six months later my mother was walking again, and we were enjoying the spring. The blue skies, warm sunshine and the bright yellow mimosa, and the palest pink almond blossom, covering the trees like snow, were a real benediction to us both.

The phone went in the villa one morning and a charming deep male voice announced that he had just arrived in the Algarve to retire, had I received a letter of introduction to him from one of my cousins in London? He turned out to be a very good shepherd.

Bernard Wheeler had volunteered for the Royal Air Force at seventeen at the outbreak of war. They sent him up to Oxford University to one of the oldest colleges, St. Edmund Hall, where he read astronomy and mathematics for a year before going into active service. It was part of the deal that he would use the academic knowledge to be a better pilot, do his service in the war and then return to Oxford to finish his degree. Many of the young pilots never returned.

So at eighteen Bernard was piloting huge Catalina flying boats over the Indian Ocean, searching for U boats to destroy. On his nineteenth birthday he remembers flying a nineteen hour duty. Those Catalinas held a lot of fuel.

In adversity we grow up fast. Like Mel, Bernard had known what it was to have his life on the line at eighteen. I had mentioned those brave young men in one of the few moments, when Mel actually talked about the possibility of her dying. One morning as she waited for another sickening chemo she had said to me with amazing candour, "I always knew I would die young. When I looked at the school leaving photo there seemed to be a ring round my face. But really it is OK. I have peace about it, more than others would have. Why NOT me, Mum?"

She was incredibly selfless and brave. What an attitude. All I could think of to say was, "Oh my darling, it's a bit like the eighteen year old RAF pilots in the Second World War. They fought for their lives, too. Let's just pray you're going to be a survivor, like some of them."

So it was prophetic that an ex-RAF wartime pilot should be the one to pick up the shattered pieces for me after she died. A book called "The Good Shepherd" tells a lovely story.

A young wartime pilot is lost in the dark and fog, after a terrifying and near fatal sortie over Germany. Alone in the plane, he gets back to England on one engine and cannot find his airbase. He flies round, fuel empty, when he sees the lights of another plane in the moonlight. The pilot signals to him to follow him down.

After he has landed, he finds he is in a disused airfield, all blacked out. There is no evidence of another plane....

Anyway Bernard became my good and very loving shepherd and brought kindness and joy back into my life. Having seventeen years more life experience than me, he was a great listener, and a wise one. There followed fifteen years of a marriage in which I was cherished and regained my confidence. He came to know the Lord in a powerful way. We shared Communion every day and in his final illness, he experienced the greatest healing of all, salvation.

We made our home in Portugal. But grief for Melanie was still huge in my life, compounded by heartbreak over the marriage breakdown and time spent away from my family. Meanwhile I researched every book on healing for cancer. Mel and I had known there must be a better way, and I developed my interest in the Gerson Therapy, based on detoxing and building the immune system up with fresh vegetable juices.

I did nutrition courses in London, India and San Diego. I learned yoga and meditation in India with Dr. Deepak Chopra, who had pioneered body/mind medicine in the west. I flirted with the nirvana of Buddhism and became a traditional Reiki master with the teacher's third degree. The Japanese doctor of theology who had started it had been looking for the Jesus healings, I was told. So was I!

I started to achieve peace I had not known previously. The meditation took me to levels of calm and spiritual awareness I had never found in traditional church services. But something was missing. Buddhism offers temporary escape from stress, but no absolution from sin, no saviour when we die and are answerable to God. The angel Mel had been so sure of still intrigued me. I wanted Jesus to be present in my life in a real way. But because at that time I did not know the Holy Spirit, I did not know how to feel His presence.

ALPHA!

Bernard and I were staying at the Royal Air Force Club in London on our way to do a tour of New Zealand. We went to my home London church, Holy Trinity Brompton, near Harrods in Knightsbridge. This was the church where I had worshipped as a girl working in the Houses of Parliament.

As I walked up the familiar avenue beside the Brompton Oratory, I noticed that there were many more people coming to Holy Trinity, Brompton, than there used to be when I got married there in 1965.

Inside was a revelation! Pews were gone, masses of chairs, lights ablaze, lively, great music and the church was absolutely packed with enthusiastic, smiling people! There was standing room only and the galleries above were also crowded to capacity. I learned there were five services a day which were just as busy! The congregation were mostly in their thirties, young, professional, bright, people who were chatting and laughing together. No "wierdos" here, they were vibrant and attractive and they were above all, cheerful. What a change from some congregations who look as though they have eaten bricks for breakfast!

The service started and a very dynamic former lawyer called Nicky Gumbel in a blue shirt and jeans, no robes, got up to preach. First, he asked a girl to come up and do a testimony. It was the first time I had heard anyone actually say anything spontaneously in church that was not in the prayer book! It was a bit shocking, but everyone looked relaxed and happy. I was absolutely riveted. This girl, who could have been me twenty years before, was saying how Jesus had come into her life and changed it.

She looked so happy, her face shone, and she told the story of her past life, searching for the truth. Just like me! "Seek the truth and the truth will set you free" she said quoting Jesus in John 8:32.

"Mmmmm…. interesting", I thought, "I think this is what I have been looking for."
I remembered Mel's angel. So this was why she was so confident as she died.
Nicky Gumbel then preached the Gospel as I had never heard it before. About how Jesus died on the cross to set us free, not only when we die, but right now in our lives.

It appeared that everyone in the church had done something called the Alpha Course. They had supper once a week and did this course and had groups where they discussed things, and suddenly the Holy Spirit came into their lives and they were totally changed, happy and completely at peace.

I went to the book shop in the crypt and bought a set of the Alpha audio tapes. I could not wait to get on the plane to New Zealand that night to listen to them on my Walkman. Alpha at 35,000 feet is a tremendous way to get saved! Meals were brought to me as I listened to one tape after another. Fifteen of them altogether! They are amusing, friendly, dynamic and totally life-changing. They are live recordings of Nicky Gumbel's Alpha talks at Holy Trinity Brompton.

The first thing that hit me was that the story of Jesus is true, and it requires a response from us. Not everyone goes to heaven. Only the saved. That is stated clearly in the Bible. We cannot sit on the fence. Ooops!

I realised the fact intellectually as well as in the heart. I heard all the documented evidence. He really died in Jerusalem, He really rose and all the disciples' lives were changed in that moment from despair to joy and boldness.

We flew on through the night as I listened to tape after tape.

26

And then, just as the dawn was breaking in the night sky, and the rim of the earth glowing red below, the light dawned for me. I was totally convinced that Jesus was who He said He was.

I gave my life to Jesus and asked His Holy Spirit to come into me. He filled me to overflowing. I was filled with peace and joy, all darkness evaporated and I felt a huge excitement for the future. The water I had been drinking on the flight became Living Water. I was completely and absolutely sure of my Saviour, sure He had a plan for me, and that my future was secure in Him. What a place to be!! I had never known such joy. Mel who had believed, was all right, and now I was all right. Totally life changing!

For the first time since Melanie had become seriously ill, I felt "a peace which the world cannot give." All through her illness I had wrestled with God, begging him to heal her. I had asked God where he was when my daughter died, despite all the prayer. "In the same place I was when my Son died" was the answer. I now knew just how much God loves us to have allowed his Son to die to redeem us. I also understood how He longs for His sons and daughters to be at one with him again.

It was only now as the battle was over, and I had woken up as Jacob did in his dream in Genesis 32:24. Like Jacob, I was now limping from the struggle, but now I had seen God and given my life to Him. A new journey had begun.

New Zealand was a good, honest to God, place to arrive as a new born again believer. Beautiful unspoiled countryside, mountains, lakes, rivers. And I was replaying the Alpha tapes on the long journeys we took through North and South Islands.

On the first Sunday we went to church in the Bay of Islands, and saw a familiar Alpha notice outside the church. Nicky Gumbel and someone called Emmy Wilson had been there launching Alpha in New Zealand the month before. Everyone was enthusing about Alpha. I was not alone! And years later, Emmy Wilson was to play a huge role in my life.

The Sunday after we got home to Jersey, a young missionary doctor, called Nick Wooding, came to preach at the family church. He had a South African accent, and the sheer love of Jesus just shone from his face. He told us he was working at Kiwoko Hospital in Uganda, a huge area which had been the scene of genocide in the time of Idi Amin and Milton Obote. Millions of Africans had been killed or maimed, their homes destroyed.

A bush hospital had been started by an Irish doctor who had given up his lucrative practice in Bangor to serve these people. This doctor, Ian Clarke, had written a book "The Man with the Key has Gone" printed by New Wine, which is fascinating reading.

When Ian became ill with cancer, Nick Wooding had taken his place. He was now setting up a medical training centre so that the young Ugandans could become doctors and nurses. The training programme was being hampered as they had no accommodation for them. They needed to build two sleeping blocks, one for the boys and one for the girls.

I just knew that this was the legacy Melanie would want to have left. When she was an undergraduate at London University, she had sponsored a little African boy through Christian Aid. I had promised her I would continue to do this after she died, but to my consternation the scheme did not permit sponsors to continue their aid to one particular child after the child finished school.

If I took on the Kiwoko Hospital scheme in her name, Melanie would be helping countless children. Praise God for the opportunity. After he preached, I told Dr. Nick Wooding Melanie's story, and said that I would put up the money for one of the buildings in her memory, and would try and raise the money for the second.

For many years I had been a Samaritan in Jersey, and I believe there are no coincidences, but God-incidences where God is working his purpose out. One of my past Samaritan friends, Jackie Huet, was now President of Jersey Overseas Aid. I rang Jackie and told her the story. I asked her if there was anything Jersey could do to build the second hospital. Jackie said she would ring me back.

Within an hour, the phone rang. Jackie said not only would Jersey Overseas Aid give the money for the second building, they would send a Jersey work party out to Kiwoko to build both the blocks. They would go in a few months time, at Easter. How appropriate! Melanie had died at Easter.

So began a building time for me as well as for Kiwoko. As I put the cheque in the post box in the village, I nearly passed out! Never before had I written a cheque for such an amount, and never had I been to Kiwoko. But I trusted God, and learned a vital truth - you can never outgive God.

What God did in my life from that moment on has been phenomenal! Not only did my all consuming grief become gratitude for the twenty wonderful years we had her, and a joy to know she was safe with the Lord, but I also had a quiet contentment thinking of good things that were to be done through Melanie, the young people who now had a career and hope in their lives because of her life. I was now in touch with a group of young people who were in the Jersey working party. Teachers, security men, nurses, retired postal workers and telephone engineers; they all shared the vision to make the world a better place. Light was coming back into my life.

We had a blessing for the building team in the church, and the Jersey newspaper featured Melanie's project on the front page. Instead of promoting the wearing of car safety belts, as she had done when she first appeared on the front page of this paper, now she was promoting God's safety belt.

Psalm 126:6 says *"when you go forth weeping, sowing precious seed, you will return with your sheaves, rejoicing."* Sheaves are symbolic of people in the Bible. I now felt closer to Melanie than I had ever felt before, even when she had been a sunny little girl in my arms. This was a huge Joy, like her middle name.

God tells us throughout the Bible to give. And he asks us to prove him in this.
The last book of the Old Testament, Malachi, in chapter 4 verse 2 is very clear.

"Test me in this" says the Lord God. And see if I will not open the floodgates of heaven and pour out so much blessing that you will not have room enough for it."

If only we knew the blessings that God wants to shower on us, we would be huge givers. In Luke 6:38 Jesus says

"Give and it will be given to you. A good measure, pressed down, shaken together and running over, will be poured into your lap. For with the measure you use, it will be measured to you!"

When we realise what God has given for us, his precious only son, to die for our sins, what can we give in return? Money, certainly, because all we have comes from the gifts he gave us to earn money, yes, but what about our lives? Surely we owe him those! I thought about ministry; but as a woman, divorced and with another husband? I felt so unworthy.

I was reading my Bible more and more. With the Holy Spirit now my "helper", as Jesus promised in John 15:25, I now understood it! Certain texts jumped out of the pages with utmost clarity and I had to smile in rueful and sometimes awful recognition of myself. One story really spoke to me. The woman at the well had sinned, but she brought her whole community to Jesus. How wonderful that would be. I prayed about it and was given a word of knowledge by an Australian pastor from Kensington Temple, in London, that I would have an international ministry.

Where to start? God does not believe in denominations, and Jesus prayed for believers to be one, but I needed to be trained in ministry somewhere!

Alpha, which had brought me to a living faith, was Anglican, based at Holy Trinity London. How I would love to have trained there. But because we were living in Portugal, I started my training locally. However, political factions were tearing the congregation apart. The Holy Spirit directed me back to our family church in Jersey where we had a new vicar, Bill Matthews, who is a great and dynamic man of God. He walks the walk as well as talks the talk, and has brought many non Christians to faith in many facets of his fifty year ministry. It was hard to give up our home in Portugal but we did it in obedience.

Having seen church politics wreck a church, I had no call to become a vicar with a parish. I knew God would lead me to the ministry I was to have. I trained for four years, and was then blessed by the bishop, and able to take services, preach, and administer Holy Communion in church, to groups and in hospital. I joined the Chaplaincy team at the Jersey General Hospital, and worked at my family church on Sundays.

I also represented Bible Society in Jersey, which enabled me to preach in different churches and denominations. What a privilege, what a blessing and what an opportunity to reach the lost for Jesus.

During my training in England I was paired on a project, by God-incidence, with an ex-Army colonel who had also lost a daughter to cancer, been divorced, remarried and now very strongly felt God's call on his life. It was encouraging to realise I was now with Holy Spirit filled, purpose driven people, who had led very real lives, and all come to the conclusion that God was the answer, in fact the only answer!

Towards the end of my training, I was struck with pancreatic cancer overnight. I held an island wide service at my church on Saturday 6th September 2003 for Bible Society, and served dinner to over a hundred people at the back of the church. During the evening I was attacked by vicious pain. The next day I could hardly lead the service. The pain was becoming unbearable, and I was turning yellow. I was jaundiced.

On the Monday I went to the doctor, who said "Major problem" and sent me for a scan. The diagnostic radiologist and I looked at the TV image of my pancreas. A huge tumour was evident. "Is it cancer?" I asked? I told him I had watched my daughter die of cancer. He looked me in the eye. He was sorry, but yes, it was.

Chapter Three

God's Cancer Cure

"I shall not die, but live, and proclaim what the Lord has done."
Psalm 118:17

Bernard arranged for me to be taken into King Edward VII military Hospital in London within a week. I was put on morphine and anti nausea medication. I had lost a quarter of my body weight within two weeks.

Every test was done, and scans taken. The very eminent and kind consultant skilfully and painlessly inserted a stent into a duct which had been cut off by the tumour, and this relieved the acute jaundice. Then I was released from the hospital and, in the politest way, sent home to die. The consultant told me there was nothing more that could be done. The tumour filled the head of my pancreas, so a Whipple's operation was not possible. Radiation and chemotherapy were not an option, he told me. After the suffering they had caused Melanie I would not have entertained either anyway.

The day after I came out of hospital was Sunday and I joined Bernard who was staying at the Royal Air Force club in Piccadilly. The receptionist was so kind; she went to church with her mother and they lit candles for me. The faith and compassion of strangers is an unexpected joy and comfort.

My good shepherd, Bernard, guided me back to Holy Trinity Brompton, my home church when I had been working in the Houses of Parliament in my early twenties. After the service, I asked for prayer and Emmy Wilson, a gracious woman who is head of pastoral care, came forward with a kind smile. She listened to my story and then she prayed powerfully for me, as befits a woman who has started "Alpha in Prisons" in UK and around the world. Many hardened and hopeless criminals have changed their lives radically and come to repent, and seek salvation, the essence of the

Christian life, through Emmy and the many teams she has trained around the world.

I had been baptised in the River Jordan previously for fire on my ministry and recognise Holy Spirit power. As Emmy prayed, the Holy Spirit filled me from the top of my head to the soles of my feet. The tears poured down my face and I knew the absolute certainty, the comfort and peace that only God can give. But the dragging, remorseless pain was still there.

Emmy turned to Bernard and asked if he was on the internet. He affirmed he was.
"Look up www.anticancerinfo.co.uk, she said. "It's based on Genesis 1:29 and 30. That is the only thing in the natural that can save Felicity." She then told us she had been a nurse at the Westminster Hospital in London before she became a pastor.

When we got back to the RAF Club I went to my bed to rest. I looked up Genesis 1:29 and 30 in my Bible. God has just created man and tells him what to eat.

"Behold, says the Lord God, I give you every seed bearing plant on the face of the earth and every tree that has fruit with seed in it. They will be yours for food. And to all the beasts of the earth and all the birds of the air and all creatures that move on the ground - every thing that has the breath of life in it - I give green plant for food. And it was so. God saw all that he had made and it was very good."

Bernard went to the computer room to look up the websites. He came back an hour later with sheaves of paper. We poured over the information together, and the more I read about B17 the more interested I became. It made sense. It spoke of building up the immune system instead of shattering it with surgery, chemotherapy and radiotherapy. Or cutting, poisoning and burning, to be more precise.

Remembering Melanie, I wondered if this was the healing we had been looking for. Lettuce leaves, as the professor of oncology had scoffed, and also the seeds of fruits and vegetables as recommended by God when he created us in Genesis 1:29 and 30. Seeds, raw vegetables, fruit and green plants.

The website was full of information on healing the body with living enzymes, about carrot juice and green juices, which were the basis of the Gerson Therapy. Bible believing biochemists had isolated the essence of the seeds and made them into a liquid called laetrile, which could be given intravenously.

I only had a few weeks to live, and we lost no time. The next morning Bernard helped me into the Land Rover and we drove down to Surrey to meet a woman whose family had been healed with these seeds. Friends heard about the B17 healings and begged her to supply them with the humble little yellow apricot kernels, too. She grows the apricots, which turn out to be the world's richest source of B17, on her farm in South Africa, and supplies these natural, life giving kernels in Europe. She lived in a place called Hurtmore, which I thought was appropriate. I could not have hurt more!

However she proved to be a friendly and efficient South African. Ten minutes later I was tasting my first apricot kernels, which were quite bitter, with natural dried apricots to chase them down. The rest of the morning she educated me into a whole new understanding of cancer. I was being given intelligent, positive information about healing. It resonated as being very, very true. It was also the Word of God!

We drove back to London and I phoned Mexico to order the ampoules of the B17 liquid, laetrile, to be sent direct to Jersey. I asked the London consultant if he knew about B17. He looked at me intently. "I cannot tell you that I know about it," he said in measured tones. "But I support you in what you want to try." I assumed that in his guarded words he did know about B17 but was constrained from advocating it because it was not "consensus" medicine. In my spirit I knew it was right.

The next problem was to find a doctor in Jersey who was prepared to give the laetrile intravenously.

My regular doctor knew nothing about it. He looked it up in his drug directory and informed me that it was cyanide and on no account would he give it to me! Tests had proved useless he said.

But by now I had ordered and received two life-saving books in the post, "Cancer, Why We´re Still Dying to Know the Truth" by Philip Day and "World Without Cancer" by G. Edward Griffin. I was becoming a little more informed on this subject than a doctor simply trained in general practice. I now understood from Day and Griffin that cyanide is only released from laetrile if triggered by cancer cells in the body, and is not toxic to any other cell.

I also learned that far too little B17 had been given, far too late, in cancer tests, as had been done when the medical establishment tried to discredit Vitamin C in tests years before. Millions of sailors had died of scurvy until it was found that scurvy was a deficiency disease, caused by lack of vitamin C. When limes were taken on long voyages, the Vitamin C they contained protected the sailors from scurvy. The sailors ended up being called "limeys!" Eventually a scientist called Linus Pauling won the Nobel Peace Prize for proving that vitamin C was a vital constituent in the human diet.

So I was not phased by the doctor's reluctance, only disappointed at his ignorance and refusal to consider this life saving natural product. I tried another doctor who was a friend. The same response, very sceptical. He was so very sorry to see me so ill. A heartfelt hug, and a kiss on both cheeks, but no B17. The Hospice, he assured me, was very caring. The pain consultant there could cut the nerves for me as a last resort when the morphine no longer worked! Great, just what I wanted to hear.

Then I remembered a woman doctor called Anne Curtis, who had been kind in the Hospice when a very dear friend had died there the previous Christmas Day. Anne, who was in the same medical practice as their regular doctor, had stayed quietly and supportively with Bob and Fran as Bob gently passed away, his immune system destroyed by many chemotherapies. When Fran thanked her and asked her if she didn't want to go and enjoy her own Christmas celebrations, she replied that this was a more meaningful way to spend the day. Fran was impressed and so grateful to her for her sensitive company that sad afternoon. I met Anne through Fran soon afterwards.

Anne also wind surfed during the Jersey summers with my son on the long sandy beach at St. Ouen. I rang her to tell her I needed B17 urgently and she sighed.

"I've just lost a patient who had laetrile too late" she said.

"I'm feeling really down, and I'm going to take a week off with my sister in France".

"Anne," I said, "please, please give me these ampoules of B17 when you come back. I've had no damaging chemo, I believe the B17 will work, and I am running out of time very fast!"

A week passed and she had not rung me. The ampoules had arrived and were waiting. I rang her again. "OK" she said, if you really want to do it, I'll give it intravenously. But I'll have to come very early morning before my surgery.

7 a.m. all right? Every other day, including Sundays."

Wonderful! The Hospice kindly loaded a drip stand, and Anne got the saline and di-methyl sodium oxide (DMSO) and Vitamin C from the hospital and pharmacies.

I read the exact regime recommended by the Oasis of Hope Cancer Hospital in Mexico.

Three to four grams of laetrile (B17) were to be infused daily or at least four times a week with DMSO and vitamin C. If infusion or injection was not possible, six tablets of 500 gram B17 tablets were to be taken daily. It was also recommended to eat ground apricot kernels, the richest source of B17. These must be started gradually, building up to the maximum dose recommended for individual height and weight of the body.

I also learned the vital importance of taking two cancer fighting pancreatic enzymes, trypsin and chymotrypsin three times a day. When we have eaten a diet rich in animal protein, our own supplies of trypsin and chymotrypsin are used up in digesting the meat or fish, leaving the body vulnerable to cancer. This is why it is so important to stop eating animal protein when we have cancer.

I was also introduced to Green Barley juice – developed by Dr Yoshihide Hagiwara, the Japanese pharmacologist and physician. Barley grass is the essence of green plant, and young barley shoots contain more chlorophyll, enzymes, minerals, amino acids, vitamins, and phytochemicals than any other green plant, providing nutrition and promoting detoxification.

I started to take fresh carrot and apple juice three times a day (add fresh garlic juice for protection against colds), and vitamin C capsules to bowel tolerance, together with 75,000 international units of Vitamin A and 1000 mg of natural Vitamin E in its natural form, alpha d-tocopherol.

Cancer cells cannot survive in an oxygenated body, so to oxygenate the body, Pangamic acid 100 mg is recommended three times a day at end of each meal. The regime also includes one antioxidant after each meal to support the immune system.

A Canadian nurse called Renée Caisse had found some years ago that native Indians were curing cancer with certain herbs. She formulated these herbs into a drink which she called "Essiac" the letters of her name spelt backwards. It is recommended that this be drunk as a tea during the day.

As cancer cells are destroyed by the hydrocyanic acid they need to be eliminated from the body, and the liver bears the brunt of this detoxification process. It is therefore recommended to take Silymarin (Milk Thistle) to help the liver detoxify itself.

The quickest way to detoxify the body is, however, body-temperature coffee enemas. Simple enema kits can be bought and once one has felt the instant pain relief and feeling of revitalisation, this is adopted as a daily routine. If you shower the outside of your body for hygienic reasons, how much more necessary to shower internally! We have 27 feet of intestine which get increasingly clogged up through life. This is the cause, many doctors believe, of most disease. Coffee enema's are recommended instead of distilled hot water, for extra detoxification. Coffee, being a stimulating poison and diuretic to the system when ingested into the body by mouth, draws poisons out of the colon without harming the body, in elimination. There is only one healthy place to take coffee and it is not through the mouth!

Another powerful nutrient is flax seed, which can taken by the spoon or on salads, or more palatably in 1000 mg capsules. Shark cartilage is also recommended, three with each meal. World without cancer UK have put together a daily complete nutrient called Preven-ca which contains alfalfa, milk thistle, boldus, grape seeds, carrot, and garlic. See www.worldwithoutcancer.org.uk.

Men with prostate cancer have seen their PSA drop back to normal when they add 30 drops of saw palmetto in distilled water twice a day.

My pancreatic cancer had made me so ill that I could not eat, and I found juices wonderfully healing and nourishing. They still form the basis of my diet. Suddenly my deficiency of living enzymes was being restored, through freshly juiced carrot and apple juices, and green barley juice, available from Rev. Eric Bowtell at www.healthyliferesources.com. For my particular cancer, I found pineapple juice, containing bromelain was particularly good for the digestion.

After thirteen intravenous treatments, I started to improve. Slowly, I began to drink home made soups made from broccoli, cabbage, tomatoes and onions, and eat mashed carrots and brown rice. My treat was fresh apricot juice, the natural source of the B17 I was taking.

Sugar, salt, caffeine, cooked foods, animal protein and alcohol, I learned, contribute to our frighteningly high cancer rates. I eat 80% raw and alkaline, and only 20% cooked (lightly steamed) vegetables, which are also alkaline. It takes only a week to get on to raw alkaline Genesis diet, but when one does, the benefits are fantastic and one never wants to lapse into sickness again!

I was trusting God for every day. I took Holy Communion every morning, prayed and read healing texts in the Bible. I did the Compline Service every night before sleeping. Rosemary, a dear friend, sent me a CD of Benny Hinn reading the best known healing texts from Genesis to Revelation, and I listened to these on the earphones of my Walkman at night. I was saturated in the Word and prayer.

Psalm 103 was my greatest encouragement.
Praise the Lord, O my soul.
In all my innermost being, praise His holy name.
Praise the Lord, O my soul and forget not all his benefits.
Who forgives all your sins,
Heals all your diseases,
Redeems your life from the pit,
Crowns you with love and compassion
And restores your strength like the eagles.

Never had I been so glad to be a Christian. I knew I was saved either way. If I died I would be saved by Jesus, my advocate in heaven when I came before God's judgment. And I honestly believed that God could heal me against all the odds, to be a witness for him. I watched the dawn each day with a new sense of wonder. What did God want me to do with this special gift, with so few days left to me?

However, totally at peace, I began to heal. Within two months I was well enough to fly to Portugal, to our home in the sun. To begin with I did not have the strength to climb the stairs and had to sleep on the sofa, but to wake up in the morning to feel the sun through the tall pine trees and see the bright blue skies through the purple bougainvillea was wonderfully uplifting.

A doctor friend in Portugal met me socially. He was somewhat perturbed when I casually mentioned I was recovering from pancreatic cancer! As far as the medical profession is concerned, nobody does. He insisted I had a scan which I reluctantly agreed to. He and the radiographer were amazed. The tumour had shrunk to a small scar. They looked at the previous scans I had brought from the hospital in London, and said that if the tumour had not been arrested I would have been dead within three weeks.

I rang the consultant in London to tell him the good news, but he was non committal. He wanted me to fly to London immediately so they could do more biopsies. I told him very politely that God had healed me through the B17 and I had no intention of letting more doctors probe into the tumour site. I now knew that this is a good way of spreading cancer cells. He said it was a medical mystery and I said no, it was a miracle. It was God's Word. If I had not learned about the Genesis diet and its derivative, laetrile B17, I would be dead!

What astounded me was the ignorance of the medical profession in the face of God's Word, and their refusal to recognise the work of many scientists, and the thousands of cures that are taking place all over the world.

I had learned so much about the history of natural cancer therapies from Philip Day's wonderfully informative book "Cancer, why we're still dying to know the truth" available from www.credence.org. I learned that a Professor John Beard of Edinburgh University had discovered over a hundred years previously that when we hurt ourselves our bodies automatically initiate a healing procedure. We all have stem cells in our bodies that have been arrested at the embryonic stage and not yet gone on to develop into blood, skin, bone, or any other body part.

When we need to heal, oestrogen stimulates these embryonic stem cells to begin rapidly multiplying, forming cell masses that Beard called "trophoblasts". These trophoblastic cells have the ability to form into any body part and so repair the damage and seal off the injury.

When the repairs are complete, the healing process is terminated by two enzymes from the pancreas, trypsin and chymotrypsin. They destroy any remaining trophoblast, preventing this cell multiplication process continuing any further.

What an infinitely intelligent Creator we have. As Psalm 139 says, *"we are fearfully and wonderfully made by God."*

Beard also discovered that if our levels of these vital pancreatic enzymes are depleted, there is a possibility that the healing process may not terminate, resulting in continued multiplication of the trophoblastic mass now known as a tumour. Cancer.

Beard had also discovered that pregnancies have an identical mode of operation to healing in so far as these stem cells are concerned. He had found that at the commencement of a pregnancy the hormone oestrogen stimulates these stem cells to rapidly multiply into trophoblasts. The purpose of trophoblastic cells in pregnancy is to etch away part of the uterus that the embryo may attach itself and continue to develop. Around the 56th day of pregnancy the baby's pancreas comes on line producing the two enzymes trypsin and chymotrypsin.

Once again, these two enzymes terminate the trophoblastic multiplication of these cells. Now their task is ended and the pregnancy continues as normal. And Beard had discovered one further thing. If the baby's pancreas fails to produce these two enzymes both the mother and her baby die as an uncontrolled proliferation of trophoblast cells - cancer.

Beard's conclusion was therefore that cancer is an oestrogen instigated healing process that simply had failed to terminate on completion of its task. One wonders what he would have thought of women being given extra oestrogen as hormone replacement therapy and the contraceptive pill.

Secondly, Beard discovered that cancer is also a pancreatic enzyme deficiency problem. The pancreatic enzyme deficiency in our bodies is primarily caused by a diet rich in animal proteins which require both of these enzymes trypsin and_chymotrypsin as part of the digestion process. So we should avoid animal food loaded with fat, toxins and oestrogens used to plump up the animal for market.

God's word in Genesis 1.29 and 30 was now vindicated scientifically. We are to eat plant food and we are to eat it RAW.

A raw, plant based diet keeps us healthy, but an animal protein based diet, particularly when it is cooked and loses all living enzymes, causes sickness. Beard continued to successfully treat cancer patients with pancreatic enzymes for the rest of his life.

Then in the 1950's, an American biochemist called Ernst Krebs, well known to medical students for the "Krebs Cycle", took up the research in Nevada, USA. He was studying the absence of cancer in certain non-industrialised peoples. There are currently tribes on earth like the Hunzas, who do not have cancer. When these people start to eat a western diet, high in animal protein, they succumb like the rest of us.

What were they doing in their natural societies that was protecting them?

Krebs discovered that the Hunza people ate a lot of apricots, in fact they gauged their wealth by the number of apricot trees they owned.

But what caught Krebs attention was that they never ate the fruit without cracking open the pit and eating the seed of the fruit. The seed, as God directs in the first chapter of Genesis!

The seed, Krebs found out, contained hydrocyanic acid a compound found in the seeds of fruit excluding citrus, along with 1,400 other foods that were freely available in the western world and now no longer being consumed in sufficient quantity. It is rare to find grapes with seeds in supermarkets. These cancer curing seeds are being genetically modified out of our grapes.

Kreb's work on hydrocyanic acid led him to discover an amazing phenomenon. This substance contained in the seeds of common, non citrus, fruits, when eaten in sufficient quantities, was selectively toxic to trophoblasts, yet did not affect healthy tissue at all. Krebs named the active principle in hydrocyanic acid "Laeo-mandala-nitrile" or "Laetrile".

The technique Laetrile uses to kill cancer cells is simple and ingenious. Krebs found that cancer cells are distinguishable from healthy tissue because cancer cells contain an enzyme in their protein coating that healthy cells do not possess.

And it is this enzyme in the trophoblastic cells that triggers the laetrile into releasing a combination of two poisons, hydrogen cyanide and benzaldehyde, which selectively kill the cancer cell.

Krebs also found that when laetrile came into contact with healthy tissue, far from the body experiencing toxicity from any subsequent reaction, this excess laetrile was simply broken down into two nutritious products, sodium thyo-cynate and benzoic acid which are then passed out of the body via the urine.

Laetrile offers a method by which any cancer cells in the body, no matter where they have migrated, can be selectively targeted and destroyed with no ill effects to the rest of the body and to the recovering patient. God's way is the perfect cancer cure.

Krebs, under advice from Dr. Dean Burk, co-founder of the National Cancer Institute, awarded Laetrile vitamin status, arguing that it was the vital nutrient, the absence of which would invariably bring on the metabolic deficiency state of cancer. Laetrile, to the fury of the cancer establishment, became Vitamin B17, and branded under the name Amygdalin, after "prunus amygdalus", the humble little yellow apricot.

So why is totally effective, inexpensive and gentle cancer cure not the consensus medicine of our day? Why wasn't Melanie offered it when we begged the consultant for less toxic treatment?

The answer lies in misinformation and professional arrogance, economics and greed. We discover from books like "World Without Cancer" by G. Edward Griffin and the book I have quoted, "Cancer, why we're still dying to know the Truth" by Philip Day, that there is a very powerful international drugs cartel that controls pharmaceutical companies worldwide.

Huge profits are made out of chemotherapy drugs. It is a growing market as cancer rates escalate and more people around the world are receiving medical care than ever before. The scandal is that the international cartel of pharmaceutical companies has been given, quite wrongly, the responsibility for testing new cures. They protect their interests by making it very expensive to test or patent anything new.

Moreover, natural substances cannot be patented. No money can be made out of them. Therefore, it is not surprising that the cancer establishment does not want B17 to be used. When they test B17 they use too little, too late, as they did with Vitamin C. The cancer establishment strongly disapproves of alternative medicine.

However, nobody can stop a patient trying a natural substance, and doctors are using B17 now, and saving lives as mine has been saved. B17 is being now scientifically evidenced and a complete change in the way cancer is treated is not far away. Many books have been written, web sites set up and intelligent doctors are convinced.

I have now discovered that many doctors use B17 themselves if they get cancer, but they are not, by law in some states of America, allowed to prescribe it for their patients. So the public suffers the toxic effects of orthodox medicine, and huge sums of money are spent by governments on these treatments.

If governments spent the money on educating the public on the Genesis diet, and preventative nutrition, we could largely eliminate degenerative disease!

Despite the millions given by both the public and governments to Cancer Research charities, more people are dying of cancer today than ever before. In fact more women have died of breast cancer in the last few years than all the soldiers who died in World War I, World War II, the Korean War and the Vietnam War put together.

We have been brought up to trust our doctors. To obey what they tell us to do. So we have agreed to mutilating surgery, to be burned by radiation and to be poisoned by the most toxic drugs the world has ever created. These drugs make a healthy person sick, so it is no wonder so many cancer patients die of the treatment, not the disease.

Cancers are removed only to recur sooner or later in a different site, simply because if cancer is a deficiency of our immune system, no amount of surgery, radiation or chemotherapy will make good that deficiency.

Thank God that at long last, the truth of his directives in the Bible are being recognised. *"Seek the truth"*, Jesus says, *"and the truth will set you free."* John 8:32.

Jews, Christians and Muslims all revere the first five books of the Bible, known to Jesus as the "the Scriptures". God's instructions and laws for healthy living are all there.

When I was being driven by a taxi driver from Gatwick to speak at a Christian healing seminar in England I was delighted to hear my Muslim driver, who was fascinated by my healing story, quote the actual chapter and verse himself. Would that Christians were as well versed in their Bibles! I was then privileged to be able to tell him that Jesus had risen from the dead, unlike Mohammed, whose grave he had visited, and that I worshipped a living Saviour, who had healed me. As I paid him, he said he had found the conversation so interesting that he should have paid me instead!

We find so much healing in the Bible. Not only from cancer and other degenerative disease, but from the emotional pain that is done to us through trying to live without God as our Father and Guide.

Psalm 1 says:
"Blessed is the man who delights in the law of the LORD,
and on His law he meditates day and night.
He is like a tree planted by streams of water
Which yields its fruit in season
and whose leaf does not wither
Whatever he does prospers."

I have found complete healing in the Bible, from every problem that life has thrown my way. Forgiveness is such a huge healing, and praying for the people who hurt us always works. When we think how Jesus forgave those who were torturing and crucifying him, there is absolutely nothing that we cannot forgive. And then our heavenly Father forgives us all our sins, redeems our life from the pit and renews our strength like the eagles!

As I gradually regained my strength over two years, I started living by the health directives given in the Bible. I drank only pure "living water" or pure juices that I made myself, and ate only the foods that are Biblical. I tried to buy organic, and eat the food raw, so it was still rich in living enzymes. I ate the fresh vegetables and fruit, with their seeds, and green plants, stipulated in Genesis 1:29 and 30.

I juiced them as advised in the Gerson therapy, to be better assimilated by the body. I found that the best way to take the green plant juices was in the form of Barley Grass, which was harvested at its most nutritious, freeze dried and reconstituted into a drink.

I then discovered that two million people in America were following the Genesis diet, under the name of the Hallelujah Acres www.hacres.com. They were being completely healed, not only from cancer, but from all degenerative diseases. There are miraculous cures from heart disease, the biggest killer; diabetes, a fast growing problem, due to the high sugar content of the western diet; arthritis that cripples some and causes untold misery to many; digestive problems from ulcers to irritable bowel disease, urinary tract diseases such as cystitis; and systemic illness caused by parasites and a fungus called candida albicans which affects most of us, causing immune dysfunction, and leading to serious disease.

A recently published book, The China Study, by Dr. T. Colin Campbell, a senior heart specialist, confirms the research. Populations living on natural raw fruit and vegetables nowadays, despite the pollution in China, are simply not suffering from the degenerative disease rife in the western world.

The more I read, the more convinced I became that we could heal our bodies if we give it the right building blocks, nutrition, exercise, and get our minds right.

Very few people have the time to research this vital information, and are being poisoned by some prescription drugs. A drug may cure one problem only to cause a worse one. Anne Curtis had shown me there could be a better form of medicine, and innovative doctors are now looking at natural health. It is called integrative medicine, when one uses the best of both worlds.

It is said if you want to know what your body will be like in a few years time, examine your state of mind now. And if you want to know what is wrong with your body now, think back to how your mind has been.

Proverbs 15:30 says *"a cheerful look brings joy to the heart, and good news gives health to the bones."*

I am convinced that unforgiveness and past resentments, played over and over again, damage our health and cripple our bodies, just as they twist our minds. Jesus told us to forgive that we might be forgiven. Not only does it make us acceptable to God, is heals our bodies! I pray for those who hurt me, and I have found it works every time. I can honestly say I do not bear resentment to anyone, and it's a peaceful and a very healthy place to be.

Learning to manage stress is critical! I love to read my Bible early each morning. The Bible is a living Word and it changes us as we read. I read a chapter of Proverbs each morning. Conveniently, there are exactly thirty one chapters so one can read through them every month. I also read several Psalms, surely the most beautiful poetry in the world, and they become old friends and are easy to memorise. They can be recalled when needed, and become part of day to day vocabulary. They are especially good to use when praying out loud for other people. God's Word has an anointing and power of its own.

Most beloved of all are the Words of Jesus in the gospels. Nothing compares to His wisdom, his compassion and his love. Whenever I was in pain, I used to praise God through His Word. It works every time. Fear and pain melt away before the Word. In Ephesians 6:10, where Paul tells us to put on the armour of God, he tells us to arm ourselves with the sword of the Spirit, which is the Word of God. *"Resist the devil and he will flee!"* James 4:7. We need to speak out the Word boldly, and aloud!

When I was still seeking for answers I had studied yoga and meditation. I even went to India to do a meditation course. Blanking out was seen as the ultimate experience, and a welcome respite from ones anxieties. It was! With practice, one could get into what the teacher called "The Gap" with increasing ease.

But something was lacking. Something absolutely critical. Life necessitates dealing with issues and blanking out does not obliterate them. They have to be faced sooner or later. Death has to be faced, and so does sin. Life without Jesus means life without salvation when we die, and no answers to life's problems in this world.

Denial does not solve anything. Only Jesus does. And He solves everything. Nothing and no one is too bad to be forgiven. He stretches out His nail pierced hands in love to us, just as we are. And by His Grace, and His Grace alone, we are made right with God. That is true and lasting healing.

Chapter Four

His Story

"I have set before you life and death, blessings and curses. Now choose life, so that you and your children may live." *Deuteronomy 30:19*

God's message is clear in the Bible. He has given us the gift of life, and free choice to do with it what we will. He gives us charge over the earth and all that is in it. *"Let **them** subdue and rule over all the earth"* says the Lord, right at the beginning of the Bible in Genesis 1:28.

So we are responsible for what happens on earth! If we are obedient to his Word, we are blessed, and if we are disobedient we suffer the consequences. Sickness, divorce, death, global warming, earthquakes and tsunamis are a result of what we have done to each other and to our environment. Through prayer we can communicate with God, but first we must be in obedience to Him.

The Bible is regarded as a spiritual guide that teaches us how to come to know God during our life span on earth, and how to be saved from our sin and eternal death, through the grace of his Son, Jesus Christ, the Saviour. It is also a very practical guide as to how to live here and now, so that we might have life in all abundance, as Jesus promises us in John 10:10. *"I have come that they may have life, and have it to the full."*

Jesus says quite clearly *"I am the way, the truth and the life and no one comes to the Father but by me." John 14:6.* No one else ever rose from the dead and no one has changed world history as He did. The disciples and thousands of his followers would not have suffered and died for something they did not believe. Jesus came to fulfil the prophecies in the Old Testament, the Hebrew Scriptures, and we have to go back to these original books in order to understand the New Testament.

The Bible is God's love letter to us. It is still the best seller it has always been. It is said the average British household contains 6.4 Bibles, most of them collecting dust. The British have in general turned from God, and Britain lost its Empire and the respect of the world when it stopped being a truly Christian country.

But the Bible is still and always has been, the truth we are searching for. People in the hills of Asia who have heard about Jesus are walking four hours to come and hear the Bible read to them. Their greatest possession would be a Bible of their own. It is a living Word, which becomes alive in us and changes our lives. We don't judge the Bible, the Bible convicts and judges us as we read.

The Bible recounts a journey. Man, represented by Adam, starts off in the Garden of Eden, amongst fruit trees, as recounted in Genesis, the first book of the Bible.

There was no sin in the garden. Nothing died, and nothing was killed. All was perfection, and we were given the right diet of vegetables, fruit, seeds and green plant that we have read about in Genesis 1:29 and 30.

After men and women sin, pruning is necessary.
Jesus tells us in John 15:1-8 *"I am the true vine: and my Father is the gardener. He cuts off every branch in me that bears no fruit, while every branch that does bear fruit he prunes so that it will be even more fruitful…. I am the vine; you are the branches. If any man does not remain in me , he is like a branch that is thrown away and withers. Such branches are picked up, thrown into the fire and burned."*

The journey ends in the last book, Revelation 22:2, in a garden with *"a fruit tree bearing twelve crops of fruit, yielding its fruit every month. "And the leaves of the tree are for the healing of the nations."*

So healing is there, all through the Bible, for those who will understand.

Between Genesis and Revelation we read the stories of countless people just like ourselves, either being obedient and being blessed, or complicating and wrecking their lives with bad choices. Their bad choices compound each other. Lives are ruined, homes are shattered, and everyone blames everyone else, as they usually do when things go wrong.

Adam blames Eve, Eve blames the snake and the snake does not have a leg to stand on... The world, male dominated, has liked to blame Eve. However, biblical scholars find that Adam is really to blame. God had made Adam guardian of the garden. Adam should have stopped the snake entering, and protected Eve from being led astray. However, Eves don't always allow their Adams to wear the fig leaves!

We know that much of the lack of discipline in society today, the unprecedented crime committed against children, and also violence perpetrated by children, stems from the absenteeism of fathers. Too often we have bred a fatherless, rootless, spoiled and wild generation, unrepentant and in many cases, completely unaware of their sin. They have not been taught or disciplined by their parents and now they are not being taught or disciplined by their schools.

However, when many of these young people hear the truth of the Gospel, and realise God is a loving, merciful but just and holy, it resonates as being true. We all know in our hearts that sin will have to be punished, that there will be a reckoning.

Then we realise our need for a Saviour and want to give our lives to Jesus who has taken the dreadful punishment for us. It is not an option to sit on the fence. We have to acknowledge him our earthly existence, or on the day of judgement, he will not acknowledge us. He says *"Then I will tell them plainly: I never knew you. Away from me, you evil doers!"* Matthew 7:23.

Some young people even bring their parents into belief! Several generations now have been brought up in a world with phoney values. However, there are never enough houses, yachts, parties, drugs, lovers, titillation and alcohol to satisfy. All man-made pleasure fails. Even the good, kind people we love eventually die.

We cannot get to heaven in these earth suits, and without salvation they are lost to us for ever.

The book of Ecclesiastes 1:11 laments, *"Everything is meaningless"*. When all has been tried and considered, Ecclesiates concludes *"fear God and keep his commandments."* Therein lies our joy, our contentment, and our salvation. The people we love who die will be with us in eternity. That is God's promise to believers.

Dulling the pain with drink and drugs has become endemic in our society but addictions only compound our problems.
Proverbs 23:29-35 puts it graphically:

"Who has woe? Who has sorrow?
Who has strife? Who has complaints?
Who has needless bruises? Who has bloodshot eyes?
Those who linger over wine,
Who go to sample bowls of mixed wine.
Do not gaze at wine when it is red,
When it sparkles in the cup, when it goes down smoothly!
But in the end it bites like a snake, and poisons like a viper".

Proverbs has thirty one chapters, one for each morning of the month. Most of our wise and pithy sayings come from the Bible, and they hit the spot every time!

The final chapter of Proverbs features the wife of noble character. Far from being old fashioned, we find that she is very modern; an industrialist, importer, real estate agent, investor, wine grower, trader, manufacturer, teacher, manager and provider. Above all she fears the Lord!

The Bible is full of graphic tales. The story of the Tower of Babel, built to honour men instead of God, teaches us that when we are proud our efforts come to nothing. Just as the tower failed because the people could not understand each other, so our society breaks down when each group is self seeking; when we do not speak "the same language."

One man in the Bible, however, stayed faithful to God. His name was Abram and when he was very old, he started a long journey to find God. God eventually breathes His Holy Spirit into this elderly man and he becomes *Abraham*. This is the plural of his name in Hebrew, and God tells him he will be the father of a great nation; a multitude as great as the stars in the heavens.

Abraham fathers two sons despite his age. Ishmael, from whom the Arab nations descend, born outside the covenant to a slave woman Hagar, and Isaac, from whom the Jewish nation descends, born of his true wife, Sarah, within the covenant.

The enmity between these two sons has existed ever since, and is culminating in the final war in the Middle East over Jerusalem. It is prophesied in the Bible, and should not come as a surprise. The Bible is more up to date than tomorrow's newspaper.

The lawful son Isaac and his seed become the chosen few, the treasured possession of God, the Jewish people.

When they are disobedient, they are in bondage, and for 430 years the children of Israel suffer as slaves to Pharoah in Egypt. When they repent, God calls Moses to rescue them. When Pharoah refuses to let them go, God imposes ten plagues on their oppressors. The plagues culminate in the death of the firstborn in each household not protected by the blood on the wooden lintel, a mark of the covenant with God. This foreshadows Jesus' blood on the wooden cross.

The Israelites are then released by Pharoah, only to be stopped by his forces again at the Red Sea. God parts the waters, and they walk to safety, in the great exodus, only to endure 40 years wandering in the Wilderness, before Joshua leads them into the Promised Land of Canaan.

From this line comes David, the shepherd boy who becomes King of Israel, and eventually Mary, the mother of Jesus and her husband to be, Joseph, his earthly stepfather. Through the Holy Spirit covering her, Jesus himself is born.

The Jews do not recognise him as their long awaited Messiah, because he has not come with power, but in humility as a baby. He is then scorned by the Jewish people and crucified by them. Because of their disobedience in not recognising Jesus as Messiah, disaster comes on the Jewish people, as Deuteronomy foretold to all who are disobedient. Only the Messianic Jews who are true followers of Jesus, who is called "Yeshua" in Hebrew, are right with God.

The time gap between the Jews crucifying Jesus and His second coming in glory to judge the world, is our chance for salvation, as Gentiles. We have the opportunity to hear the Gospel and come to faith. We are the shoot grafted on to the main stem, Israel. Romans 11.11. It is the disbelief of the Jews that has made possible our belief and our salvation. And when we acknowledge the Old Testament laws God originally made for His People, our health, wealth and relationships are made right.

This is the knowledge that saved my life, and the lives of countless others, when we came into obedience with God's laws.

Exodus 23:25 and 26 says *"If you listen carefully to the voice of the Lord your God and do what is right in his eyes, if you pay attention to his commands and keep all his decrees, I will not bring on you any of the diseases I brought on the Egyptians, for I am the Lord who heals you."*

Through the blood covenant, symbolised by male circumcision in the Old Testament, and symbolised by Jesus' life blood in the New, God blesses his chosen people, as long as they remain obedient.

The blood is sacrosanct, the Bible tells us. We are never to eat the blood of any bird or animal. Leviticus 7:26 *"If anyone eats blood, that person must be cut off from his people."* How interesting that toxicologists recognise that toxins are carried in animal and bird blood, and red meat should never be eaten. In the Jewish tradition meat is slaughtered so that the blood is completely drained, and then the meat is well roasted. In biblical days meat was only eaten in celebrations.

The Jews learned that sin has to be paid for by blood, and had a system of sacrificing an innocent animal – a scapegoat - to atone for their sin. The people are made right by atoning for their sin on the Day of Atonement, the holiest day of the year, known in Hebrew as Yom Kippur.

The High Priest would enter the Holy of Holies in the Temple on that day once a year, which is the most solemn day of prayer in the Jewish calendar. In great fear of being struck dead, the High Priest would pass beyond the veil dividing the Holy Place from the Holy of Holies, offering sacrifice and incense on behalf of the people.

So fearful were they that the High Priest would be struck dead in the presence of God in the Holy of Holies, that he wore a robe with tiny bells on the hem. If he stopped moving and the bells stopped ringing, the people would extricate his body from the Holy of Holies by ropes that they had tied around his ankles.

The Temple was destroyed by the Romans in 70 AD, just as Jesus prophesied. All that remains of it now is the Western Wall, or Wailing Wall, where millions go to pray from around the world.

But pray and atone as we might, there is still a problem. God is completely just, completely holy as well as merciful. Try as we might, we are simply not pure enough to atone ourselves, and the innocent scapegoat is not a just settlement.

Throughout history, until the Messiah came two thousand years ago, there was no way that man could become right with God. It is impossible for man to remain obedient. Our human nature causes us to sin and we are irrevocably separated from God.

So God in His infinite mercy, sent Jesus, the Messiah, who had been prophesied throughout the Old Testament, to show the way and to die for the sins of the people. When Jesus died on the cross, the veil in the Temple, a substantial curtain, was rent in two. Jesus had opened the way to God and made it possible for us to approach Him without a barrier.

Jesus, the Messiah, is the only one ever to have lived without sinning, the perfect sacrifice, known as the Lamb of God. Only through His Blood can we be washed clean and saved from God's wrath when we are judged. His blood, like ours, as any haemotologist will tell you, gives life and carries away the rubbish out of our lives.

Jesus will be our advocate on Judgement Day, which is to come at the end of the world, when all our sins are revealed for all to see. That is the Gospel. That is the story of salvation; the greatest and eternal healing, through the cross.

But the cross also has a back, and it is the back of the cross, the beaten and bloody back of Jesus, which heals us. *"By His stripes we are healed,"* says Isaiah 53. Many are healed by believing in Jesus as their saviour and also their healer.

During the three years of His ministry on earth, Jesus healed all who asked, and through others faith raised the dead. Faith was the criterion and still is. Above all, He is the only one ever to have risen from the dead, as witnessed by thousands whose lives were completely changed by Him.

Only through Jesus, as Advocate when we die and stand in judgement before God, will any of us be saved from our sins.

The Bible shows us that God is a holy and just God, as well as a merciful God. Herein lies our problem. Our sin cannot just be wiped out, someone has to pay the penalty.

As John 3:16 says,
"and God so loved the world that He sent his only beloved Son, Jesus, to die for us so we could have eternal life."

There are 332 major prophecies in the Old Testament which describe the life and death and resurrection of Jesus in detail, hundreds of years before he came to earth.

He would be born in Bethlehem Micah 5:2; of a virgin, Isaiah 7:14; He would become a prophet like Moses, Deuteronomy 18:15; enter

Jerusalem on a donkey, Zechariah 9:9; be rejected by his own people, Psalm 118:22; be betrayed by one of his followers Isaiah 53:8; be silent before his accusers Isaiah 53:7; spat on by his enemies Micah 5:1; taunted and mocked Psalm 22.7; crucified Psalm 22:14; suffer with transgressors and pray for his enemies Isaiah 53:12; offered vinegar and gall as a pain killer Psalm 69:21; have his garments divided by lot between his torturers Psalm 22:18; have no bones broken during this awful death Numbers 9:12; and to die as an offering for sin Isaiah 53:5; and be raised from the dead Psalm 16:10; sit on God's right hand Psalm 110:1.

These prophecies, made so long before Jesus lived, and fulfilled by Him in every detail, prove beyond all reasonable doubt that Jesus was the long awaited Messiah. Once one is convinced that Jesus was the Messiah, we cannot get saved by his blood fast enough. It is the only way out of our sin!

But we can hardly sit smugly in our security and not care about others. The responsibility of Christian belief is to bring unbelievers to belief in Christ as their saviour so that all may share in salvation. How can we sit at the Feast if our brother or sister, a parent, a child or a friend whom we love, is left outside?

As Jesus says in *John 4:34 "the field are ripe for harvest."* Never have so many come to believe in Jesus as the Messiah as in these last few years. Christian TV, beamed by satellite into every continent, has reached more with the Gospel than ever before.

The church thrives despite persecution, and in Russia, India, North Korea and China many are still imprisoned and even being tortured to death because they are preaching and practising their Christian faith. House churches abound in South East Asia, where millions are now converting to Christianity. In Acts 1:8 Jesus says;
"You will witness for me in Jerusalem, in Judea and Samaria, and to the uttermost ends of the earth."

Salvation is the greatest healing. Any physical healing during our lives is a blessing, but pales compared with eternal life in heaven, as against eternal darkness and separation from God.

However, during our time on earth, the Bible tells us exactly how to live in order to have abundant life.

Thorough washing, organised sanitation, sexual hygiene, a balance between labour and rest, tithing and giving, and the food laws, are all found in the first five books of the Bible, the Torah.

In Genesis 1:29 and 30, God is explicit.
"Behold I give you every seed bearing plant on the face of the earth, and every tree that has fruit with seeds in it. They will be yours for food. And to all the beasts of the earth and all the birds of the air and all the creatures that move on the ground, everything that has the breath of life in it, I give green plants for food."

God is instructing us to eat living enzymes as our basic food. Once food is heated to over 107 degrees, it has been found to have lost all its living enzymes. And when we revert to this raw living diet, most degenerative diseases such as cancer and heart disease, diabetes and arthritis, disappear.

In Deuteronomy 8:8, God tells Moses that he is leading the children of Israel into
"a good land - a land with streams and pools of water, with springs flowing in the valleys and hills, a land with wheat and barley, vines and fig trees, pomegranates, olive oil and honey; a land where bread will not be scarce and they will lack nothing, they will eat and be satisfied.

Health is a blessing or a curse. We read in Deuteronomy 28:58-62
"If you do not carefully follow all the words of this law, which are written in this book, and do not revere this glorious and awesome name, the LORD your God, the LORD will send fearful plagues on you and your descendants, harsh and prolonged disasters, and severe and lingering illnesses.

He will bring upon you all the diseases of Egypt that you dreaded, and they will cling to you. The Lord will also bring upon you every kind of sickness and disaster not recorded in this Book of the Law, until you are destroyed. You who were as numerous as the stars in the sky will be left few in number, because you did not obey the LORD your God".

The choice is up to us. But time is running out, both for us in our finite lives of three score years and ten, and also for the world. The end will come, when Jesus returns to judge us.

"No one knows the day or the hour," Jesus says in Matthew 24:36, *"but as it was in the days of Noah before the flood, people were eating and drinking, marrying and giving in marriage, and they knew nothing about what would happen until the flood came and took them away. That is how it will be at the coming of the Son of Man. Therefore keep watch!*

After Jesus rose from the dead, He appeared to his disciples many times in many places. We see that they changed from fearful men, hiding away together, to bold evangelists, speaking in many tongues, and spreading the Good News across the world.

He told them that when He ascended to His Father, he would send His Holy Spirit to comfort and guide them. At Pentecost the Holy Spirit came and filled them, and fills us today when we ask in faith.

The apostle Paul, who had persecuted followers of Jesus Christ until he had an amazing encounter with the Holy Spirit himself, went on to evangelise Turkey, Greece, Malta and Rome, and write two thirds of the New Testament. He said in his second letter to Timothy 1:7 *"God does not give us a spirit of timidity, but a spirit of power, of love and of a sound mind."*

So it is today. Many people outside the church are today finding faith through Holy Spirit filled Alpha courses and through Holy Spirit Christian television. There is a great spiritual hunger not being filled by the ritual of traditional Sunday services. People are hurting and they are seeking real answers to life's big questions. The church needs to preach the radical Gospel, irrespective of political correctness. The more we need Him, the stronger He comes. That is why some nominal Christians are not filled with joy. They have never been in the pit and they do not know His true salvation.

Christian agencies like the Salvation Army are hugely respected for giving practical help and love to people who are in need, and as Jesus says in Matthew 25:40 when we give food, water, shelter, clothing and acceptance to those who need them, we are doing them for Him. Ask the ex drug addicts, alcoholics, prisoners of every kind, who have been set free! Then you will see the real change Christianity brings.

We don't grow in the mountain top experiences, we grow in the valleys, when we are sick, bereaved or in trouble. It is said that God whispers to us in our pleasures, speaks to us in our conscience, but shouts to us in our pain. Life usually works out as learning experiences, when we can see the big picture. The Bible helps us to do that.

Psalm 40 says: *"I waited patiently for the Lord,*
He turned to me and heard my cry.
He lifted me out of the slimy pit,
Out of the mud and mire,
He set my feet on a rock
And gave me a place to stand.
He put a new song in my mouth
A hymn of praise to our God.
Many will see and fear
and put their trust in the Lord.

To be Holy Spirit filled is our greatest joy and our greatest healing. Why not ask Jesus to fill you with His Holy Spirit today, and see the difference He will make in your life?

I prayed this prayer some years ago and the Lord has been faithful to me ever since.
Heavenly Father,
I thank you for giving me the gift of my life
and all the blessings I have and so often have taken for granted.

I am sorry for all the wrong things I have done
and I ask your forgiveness,
just as I forgive all those who have wronged me.
I come to you now as a child, offering my heart.

Thank you for sending your beloved Son Jesus to die for me and take away my sins.
I believe He rose from the dead
and that when you call me home,
I shall be with you in eternity.
Please help me to live the rest of my life as I should,
To do your will in the world, to encourage others and bring many to your salvation.

I ask and believe that Your Holy Spirit will come and live in me
as my Counsellor, my Guide and my very best friend.
Come, Holy Spirit! I love you, you are welcome in my heart!
I pray this in Jesus' precious name. Amen

Chapter Five

The Breath of Life

Genesis 2:11
"The Lord God formed man from the dust of the ground and breathed into his nostrils the breath of life."

For many years, science and religion have been at loggerheads over the Creation theory. Rebellious and sinful man found the concept of God both threatening and challenging, and wanted to disprove Him and the idea of their future judgement... Darwin's theory of evolution seemed a convenient way out.

But with space discoveries and the Hubble telescope revealing more and more of the workings of the universe, the chaos theory is no longer tenable, and scientists are coming to believe in the almighty power and infinite intelligence of a Creator.

Charles Darwin repented of his evolution theory on his death bed. Angry at the death of his daughter, he had tried to prove that God did not exist. Now evolution is discounted. Monkeys and still giving birth to monkeys, they are not giving birth to human beings!

It is interesting that NASA scientists and geologists at the University of Maryland's department of Geology and the Earth System Science Interdisciplinary Centre acknowledge a "Great Oxidation Event" in the history of earth. At that moment, scientists know oxygen was suddenly released from chemically bound elements for the first time. This sounds pretty much like the Genesis 2:11 account to me – God breathed life into man who was made of the dust of the ground.

And science proves that we truly are dust! Scientists analyse the human body as being 65% oxygen, 18.5% carbon, 9.5% hydrogen, 3.2% nitrogen and the rest are miniscule but absolutely essential salts: calcium, phosphorus, potassium, sulphur, sodium, chlorine, magnesium, iodine and iron with traces of chromium, cobalt, copper, fluorine, manganese, molybdenum, selenium, tin, vanadium and zinc. Once we die, our bodies decompose back into dust, either in the grave or in the fire of the crematorium. Dust to dust and ashes to ashes!

One of my god-daughters is an astronautical and aeronautical engineer who designs air to air guided missiles for the government. She tells me that the more you discover about outer space, the more intricate are the patterns of intelligence that control it. Our bodies constitute a microcosm of the world environment, but we can only sustain life within certain parameters such as temperature and air pressure. A few degrees difference either way, and we die.

From the moment God breathed the breath of life into Adam, our most vital requirement to maintain life on earth is the air we breathe. It is said that man can live for four months without food, four days without water, but only four minutes without air.

I watched my three babies take their first breaths and my parents, my daughter and my husband breathe their last. It is pretty basic. Without the breath of life we die. And for all the progress of medical science, doctors cannot give life. Only God can give that precious gift.

The air we breathe in the twenty first century, however, is far from the air in the Garden of Eden. The chemical pollution we now have in our air in urban areas and under flight paths are taking a terrible toll. One in every five children is now asthmatic.

The levels of air pressure and oxygen/carbon dioxide ratios are changing with disastrous consequences for life on planet earth. Scientists are also finding that even the sea is also being starved of oxygen. They have traced twenty oxygen deficient areas in the sea where marine life has died. Poisons from factory emissions have contaminated lakes and rivers, and these toxins are now draining into to the seas, destroying plankton, coral and fish. The life giving, cleansing, sea water which used to clean our beaches is slowly becoming lifeless.

The seas are vital because rain is derived from them through evaporation, which then falls as precipitation on the land. In the ever increasing drought areas of the world, rain means life. Without it, people and vegetation die. Life ceases to exist.

This lack of clean, oxygenated air in the world environment also has consequences for us in our own personal environment – our body. Cancer cells thrive in an oxygen deficient environment, and respiratory problems often lead eventually to cancer.

Statistics show that one in three of us will succumb to cancer at some stage in our life. Lung cancer is a huge problem, greatly exacerbated by the air we breathe, especially smoking.

As well as tobacco, there are thirteen other noxious chemicals that cigarette companies add to these foul smelling sticks. One is ammonia which irritates the skin, eyes and respiratory tract.

You have only to smell ammonia or have a burn from neat ammonia to imagine what it does to the lungs. Another poisonous chemical contained in cigarettes is freon, a chlorofluorocarbon used in refrigerator and car cooling systems.

However, an independent toxicologist, Dr. Barry Rumack, a professor at the University of Colorado, says the two chemicals that concern him most are ethyl furoid which has been considered as a chemical warfare agent, and sclareol which causes convulsions.

Those of us who are forced to breathe second hand smoke inhale twice as much tar and nicotine in second hand smoke as compared with mainstream. This second hand smoke also contains three times as much carbon monoxide, which robs the blood of oxygen, as well as several other suspected cancer causing substances.

Of course, smoking is like purposely stepping on a landmine. Many people have been able to stop this life-threatening, filthy, anti-social, stinking habit through www.SmokEnders.com.

Whatever the cause, there is absolutely nothing so frightening as having to struggle to breathe, to live in fear of taking any exertion or even speaking because of the huge effort needed in drawing the next breath, despite using relievers such as salbutamol, known as Ventolin, in an inhaler or a nebuliser.

I have had to fly many hours due to my home and work being abroad. Following a pulmonary embolism which I had after flying four flights in three days, I developed breathing problems labelled "asthma" by doctors when I was sixty.

I was prescribed all the usual inhalers, preventers and relievers, and steroids called prednisolone, all of which have harmful side effects. Ventolin increases the heart rate, and steroids depress the immune system, making one more prone to repeated infections, which further damage lungs that are already compromised. However, when the breathing is severely compromised, there is no alternative but to take the drugs and one is grateful for them. The vicious cycle can, however, deteriorate until one can develop COPD, chronic obstructive pulmonary disease, which used to be called emphysema.

The worst part of this for me was that I could not lie down to sleep. As soon as I lay on my back and my lungs were compressed, I was struggling for breath and had to sit up. Finally I did not attempt to go to bed, but slept sitting up in a chair. Eventually in desperation I bought a hospital bed to prop me up through the nights. For six years I was awake every two hours having to inhale medication, sit forward, and sip hot drinks until I could clear the congestion and the breathing eased.

I was getting exhausted, and I believe that this was when the cancer developed. Cancer cells thrive in a deoxygenated environment, which is why exercise, preferably in the fresh air is so important. The cruel irony is that if you have asthma you cannot exercise as you should. I had always played a lot of sport in the fresh air, and it had done a lot to keep me healthy. It is a discipline.

As with everything in life, success depends on practice and focus. Learning to play tennis had required hitting balls against a practice wall for hours to develop muscle memory before I was able to play proficiently.

Similarly, I had had to hit thousands of golf balls before I learned to hit the ball a long way in the right direction on drives, to place the ball accurately on approach shots and to putt smoothly to the hole on the greens. I still need to practise!

There are so many golfing analogies to our Christian faith! We need to keep on the straight and narrow of the fairways. We also need to keep out of bunkers on a golf course which are so similar to the bunkers of life, sin! Keeping focussed is the only way of getting out of the bunker, and the experience of having being in one concentrates the mind to avoid them in the future!

So when I became ill, I really focussed on healing. Learning what was going to heal cancer, and then practising that knowledge, being disciplined, constantly *believing* for healing, is really important.

Prayer is a way of focussing entirely on God, our Creator, praising him for his blessings, and seeking his healing. He created us and only he can heal us. Our times are in his hands! When I had heard about the Genesis diet I knew it made sense. It was God's Word and I therefore had trust that it would heal me. This is the way God intends us to live and I simply followed his instructions.

I had been sent to specialists for my severe breathing problems and was diagnosed with COPD, Chronic Obstructive Pulmonary Disease and given a new inhaler called Spiriva. I also used Santa Herba, the Holy Herb, available from Lehning, the German homeopathic company, which I took four times a day.

During the six years I had severe breathing problems, I found other helpful natural remedies. I have always believed that God has given us every healing thing we need, if only we know where to look. Revelation 22:1 and 2 says clearly:

"Then the angel showed me the river of the water of life, as clear as crystal, flowing from the throne of God and of the Lamb down the middle of the great street of the city. On each side of the river stood the tree of life, bearing twelve crops of fruit, yielding its fruit every month. And the leaves of the tree are for the healing of the nations. No longer will there be any curse."

My husband found a bronchitis cure on the internet which was based on inhaling the steam of three essential oils, cinnamon, clove and thyme. This is wonderfully clearing for the whole respiratory tract.

Cinnamon is the inner bark of a tropical evergreen tree from Sri Lanka, imported to Europe by Portuguese and subsequently Dutch setters. In ancient Egypt cinnamon was considered more precious than gold and used medicinally. Later, the Crusaders brought it back to Europe, mixing the spice with fruit and meat; the original mince pies!

Cloves are the aromatic dried flower buds of an Indonesian tree called Syzgium aromaticum. The name derives from French "clou" a nail, as the buds vaguely resemble small irregular nails in shape. Cloves are harvested mainly in Indonesia and Madagascar, also Zanzibar, India, Sri Lanka and the Spice Islands of the Moluccas. They are picked when the flower has turned crimson. As well as being used in cooking, cloves have anaesthetic and antimicrobial qualities, and are used to eliminate bad breath. Oil of cloves is still used by dentists to anaesthetize the gum prior to injecting novocaine.

Thyme was grown in monastery gardens in Southern France, Spain and Italy during the Middle Ages and used as a cough remedy, a digestive aid and treatment for intestinal parasites. It is particularly useful, therefore, when candida albicans has settled in the lungs, an insidious cause of asthma. Thyme is the active ingredient in Listerine mouthwash and Vicks Vapo-rub because of its antibacterial and antifungal properties. It loosens phlegm and relaxes the muscles in the respiratory trace.

The combination of these three powerful essential oils makes a powerful inhalation. As an emergency treatment when away from home, I saturate a tissue with the oils and put it in a small plastic airtight container and inhale as and when I want.

I also found that sniffing up a handful of a weak solution of salt water and bicarbonate of soda was very cleansing to the sinuses. Most chest infections are exacerbated by post nasal drips.

A relaxing bath with essential oils is a great preliminary to a good night's sleep. The steam in the bath helps to decongest the lungs, and relax the whole body.

Aromatherapy oils help, too. A doctor friend told me to put eucalyptus oil on the breastbone to ease breathing. I find lemon aromatherapy oil massaged lightly into the skin after the morning shower perfumes me for the day and invigorates me. As Psalm 133 says "the precious oil of anointing" harmonises us, both within ourselves and with others.

Lavender, too, is a wonderful boost to the auto immune system, and used at night is a wonderful way to end the day and eliminate insomnia.

I also researched Buteyko breathing. This is a system developed by Professor Buteyko, a Russian chest physician, to restore the correct oxygen/carbon dioxide levels in the lungs, and it works remarkably well.

Buteyko teaches us to breathe only through the nose, rather than the mouth, day and night. This is to warm the air and also filter out some pollutants through the fine hairs inside the nose.

Micropore is used to tape the mouth at night to avoid breathing through the mouth while sleeping. An added benefit to this is it completely eliminates snoring, and is a marriage saver! When asthma is bad, particularly when suffering from a cold, a Breathe Right plaster can be used to open the nostrils. Marathon runners and triathletes like my son have discovered that this greatly eases breathing under pressure, and it is a huge benefit for those with breathing problems.

Going to bed with Micropore on the mouth and Breathe Right on the nose is hardly a romantic sight, and my husband and I thought it hilarious at first. However, after many sleepless nights due to snoring and breathing problems, one learns never to run out of these products, or forget to pack them in the overnight travel bag!

Buteyko trains us to breathe out fully, and hold the breath out, something that is an anathema for asthma sufferers. But this allows the lungs to recover from the continuous onslaught of pollutants. Over time, confidence is built up and the pause between breaths grows longer and stronger, and one creates ones own "ventolin" and can clear the chest without medication.

Many asthma sufferers are able to gain complete relief with the Buteyko method and can stop using damaging ventolin and steroids. What a shame that doctors do not introduce their patients to this system. Check out www.buteyko.com

One of my dearest friends, Ruth, is a Chinese girl who was at school with me in England. She became a consultant anaesthetist, but when she retired from orthodox practice, she qualified as a doctor of acupuncture back in Hong Kong. She was very impressed with her new field of medicine, and in her retirement has developed a thriving acupuncture practice.

Ruth told me several acupuncture points for asthma and breathing problems. Some of these points, which open up the lungs, are found on various points on the ear, ankle and arm! They are very effective, and I soon became quite relaxed doing my own acupuncture.

Ruth also taught me how to cup the back and chest to loosen congestion. These cups can be bought from Chinese medicine stores, such as Acumedic in London (telephone 0207 388 6704) who have a postal service.

Acupressure is an option for those who dislike needles. The points for asthma, pain, or nausea can be pressed with a finger nail, or the cap of a biro.

Back pain can also be self treated by acupressure. Two tennis balls under the back can work wonders as one lies on the ground and moves the pressure to various points on back of the neck, the shoulders and down the back. Ruth explained that pain is a blocked energy meridian. Releasing that meridian will release the pain or energy blockage.

There is a trio of Chinese herbs called ling zhi, ku shen, and gan cao which are the basis of a fourteen herb blend used in Beijing hospitals to treat asthma. It is known as "Ashmi". A double-blind study by Mount Sinai School of Medicine in New York gave 91 patients with moderate to severe asthma either Ashmi or the conventional treatment, the steroid Presdisolone. After four weeks, both treatments had improved the patients' lung function significantly and both patient groups needed to use their inhalers less.

However, the Chinese herbs did not seem to have any side effects compared with Prednisone, which can lower adrenal function and caused patients in the trial stomach problems and weight gain. The senior investigator, Dr. Xiu Mi Li, claims, "this is the first well controlled study in which an anti-asthma Chinese herbal medicine has been found to be as effective as a corticosteroid drug."

Inhaling salty air has been known to help breathing problems, and many asthmatics prefer living by the sea. For those living inland, a new device called the Saltpipe is very helpful. See www.saltpipe. The Saltpipe contains 50-60 grams of pure salt crystals and lasts for five years based on fifteen to twenty minutes use each day. The salt crystals are found in deep salt caves found in Northern Europe.

This ceramic inhaler was invented by Hungarians, Budai and Bekefi, who both suffered from asthma and allergies. The salts clean, regenerate and heal the irritated and inflamed respiratory system by dissolving crusts and sediments. Salt dehydrates the albuminous structure of microbial cells and prevents congestion. Sniffing mildly salty water from the cupped hand well up into the sinuses several times a day and then gently blowing the nose clears infections quickly.

Those with breathing problems have to avoid infections. A three day common cold can create severe problems for an asthmatic for up to three weeks. A good way to prevent chest infections is to cleanse face and hands properly several times a day. Bible believers through the centuries have been protected from sickness, such as the plague, by following the thorough washing directed in the Old Testament. Use a scrubbing brush when washing the hands, remembering to cleanse well under the finger nails, a notorious place for germs to lurk.

Another useful tip is to use liquid soap, as cakes of soap encourage germs to linger up to forty eight hours in the slime that stays under them. Paper towelling to dry the hands is so much more hygienic than a cloakroom towel, used by one visitor after another.

Try using gloves and sometimes even a nurse's mask for travelling so as not to pick up every bug circulating in big international airports and on flights. Too often long haul travelling is blighted by picking up chest infections on the flight.

Colloidal silver is nature's antibiotic. It is excellent to spray the back of the throat, the nostrils and also the ears during the day to prevent picking up unwanted germs.

These toxins collect in the mouth overnight while one is sleeping. They can best be removed by swilling the mouth with extra virgin, cold pressed sunflower oil. Take a mouthful and swill for a full fifteen minutes. The liquefied oil has by then absorbed all the toxins. These are said to be so noxious they should not be spat into the basin, but down the loo! Follow this by cleaning the teeth and swilling with a solution of bicarbonate of soda, which makes a very good toothpaste. Bicarbonate of soda is much healthier than commercial toothpastes, some of which contain rat poison!

Magnesium, potassium and vitamins A. C and E and CoQ10 are very helpful to keep our heart and lungs working efficiently and aid breathing. Remember to walk thirty minutes a day in fresh air, preferably by the sea. Green trees are a good alternative, as they give off oxygen, but beware the pollen season! If the weather does not permit the asthmatic to exercise outside, invest in a walking machine such as an air glider, to ensure you still get your half hour of exercise each day. There are also walking tapes which use music with a varying numbers of beats, or steps, per minute.

However, nothing cured my emphysema until I went on the Genesis Diet. I started taking flaxseed oil, derived from the seeds God tells us to eat in Genesis 1:29. I take three 1000 mg capsules with my morning juices, another three with my lunchtime salad and the last three with my supper of vegetables. The healing was dramatic.

The medical profession say there is no cure for asthma, at best it can only be controlled. At worst, it can kill. I suffered horribly and was practically disabled for six years. I could not walk far. On a bad day I needed ventolin to get across the room. I had to have wheelchair assistance at airports when flight connections necessitated a long walk between terminals. I was dependent on the strongest "preventer" and "reliever" inhalers, plus 30 mg of damaging Prednisolone steroids every day. But six weeks on the Genesis Diet with a daily dose of 9000 mg of flaxseed oil healed me. The flax seeds are pure Genesis 1:29!

The relief and the joy was incredible. I was so grateful to God for His Word, and long to see other sufferers find relief. And once we can breathe again without effort, it's important to remember we are God's children, and ensure that every word we say, during each day, is worthy of the Breath He blesses us with.

Try breathing in His Holy Spirit, as God breathed into Adam. As you spend time alone in absolute calm and breathe the Holy Spirit in, you will find a peace that the world cannot give. It is the peace of Jesus. Praise and breathe, praise and breathe, and be blessed!

Chapter Six

Living Water

Exodus 15:22
Then Moses led Israel from the Red Sea and they went into the Desert of Shur. For three days they travelled in the desert without finding water. When they came to Marah, they could not drink its water because it was bitter - that is why the place is called Marah. So the people grumbled against Moses saying "What are we to drink?"

Then Moses cried out to the Lord and the Lord showed him a piece of wood. He threw it into the water, and the water became sweet. There the Lord made a decree and a law for them, and there he tested them.

He said "If you will listen carefully to the voice of the Lord your God and do what is right in his eyes, if you pay attention to his commands and keep all his decrees, I will not bring on you any of the diseases I brought on the Egyptians, for I am the Lord who heals you." Then they came to Elim, where there were twelve springs and seventy palm trees, and they camped there near the water.

Our lives on earth sometimes seem to consist of trudging through a desert, as the children of Israel did. So many apparent pleasures of life are a mirage, like the glistening waters of Marah must have seemed to the thirsty Israelites, until they tasted them and found them bitter. The worldly pleasures we seek look so attractive until we taste them, and find they are bitter.

God makes it clear in His Word, early in the Bible, that only He can provide Living Water for all our needs, spiritual and also physical. As we see the wood sweeten the water at Marah, it takes the wooden cross of Jesus to take away the bitterness, and give us Living Water.

Jesus says, in John 4:14 "Whoever drinks the water I give him will never thirst. Indeed, the water I give him will become in him a spring of water welling up to eternal life."

Jesus often taught in parables and He used everyday examples which the people of the time understood. The sowing of seed, the sifting of grain, the caring of sheep, and the collection of water.

In this graphic parable about living water He is addressing the Samaritan woman at Jacob's well. This woman had to come to collect water from the well in the midday heat to avoid the critical tongues of the other village women. It was the custom to collect water in the cool of the morning and again in the cool of the evening.

She was a woman of Samaria, an area despised by orthodox Jews because the Jews there had intermarried with the local women following the exile in Assyria. Samaritans they did not come to worship at the Temple but worshipped instead on Mount Gerizim.

Furthermore, as is the custom even today, orthodox Jewish men do not engage into conversation with women outside their family circle. So it was a great surprise to this Samaritan woman to find Jesus, a Jew, addressing her, asking for water.

Jesus reveals to her who He is, and also tells her that He knows everything about her. She is a woman who, like many of us, has sought love in the wrong place. In orthodox Judaic culture, she would have been ostracized from society. She is so amazed at Jesus' words that she goes back to the village, overcomes her inhibitions, and tells them to come and hear a man "who told me everything I ever did" and who can offer eternal life. The Samaritans came to the well to hear Jesus, and urged Him to stay for two days, and many of them came to believe he was the Messiah. They accepted Him, and with Him Living Water which would give them eternal life.

The amazing thing about this parable is that Jesus revealed His identity for the first time, to a woman. Just like Mary Magdalene, this woman was instrumental in bringing many to the Lord. After

His resurrection He first appeared to Mary in the garden and told her "Go tell my disciples" that He had risen. Women, like His mother Mary, the Samaritan woman and Mary Magdalene, and all believing women, whether they are wives, mothers or daughters, have a huge role in bringing people to Jesus.

Jesus said that we must be "born of water and the Holy Spirit." And of course it is through water that we are born on our earthly mothers. In our mothers' wombs we are protected by amniotic fluid and once independent, we need to keep our bodies adequately hydrated throughout life. When we come to faith and ask the Holy Spirit to fill us, we are born again in the Holy Spirit. We are empowered and guided to do the will of the Lord, and He is our comfort and our eternal joy.

Our need for water is second only to our need for air to breathe. The Holy Land is a land of many streams, and in Biblical days the water was pure and unpolluted. Deuteronomy 8:8 describes it as *"a good land - a land with streams and pools of water, with springs flowing in the valleys and hills."*

Sadly today, many areas are affected by life threatening drought, and in the industrialised world, water supplies are polluted with chlorine and fluoride. So we have to take precautions to see that our families drink only pure water. Parasites are said to affect 95% of us. 180 species live and breed in our intestines and blood and can invade the liver, brain and lungs, leading to serious disease.

When I was battling cancer I invested in a water distiller, and liked the taste and purity of this water so much that I now drink nothing else. I also use it in soups and if I am steaming vegetables. I also have a reverse osmosis unit fitted, so that all the water used in the kitchen is pure.

It is said that adults should sip a glass of pure hot water with a slice of lemon slowly every waking hour, and I find that an easy way to remind myself to drink enough water. Drinking a glass of hot water in the morning refreshes the digestive system and gives the body an internal shower. Cold water slows down our digestive system, so its good to always drink water hot or at room temperature with a slice of lemon, which is alkalising and healthy to the body. It's not good enough to just drink when we are thirsty; the body needs much more hydration than that.

Many people have cured back pain by drinking more water, which hydrates the discs and cushions the spine. Many who have suffered from ulcers have also found simple pure water healed their digestive problems. Colds and other infections are cut short by drinking adequate water.

I keep small bottles of distilled water in my handbag and my car, so that I can drink my hourly ration wherever I am.

Our blood and lymph are mainly made up of water. We are creatures that need to flow! We need to "stir our water" our lymph system, every day with exercise. Our circulation has a pump, the heart, but the lymph system, which has to cope with four times the volume of liquid, has no pump. It relies on our exercising our bodies, so we have to make an effort to stimulate the flow of lymph several times a day. A rebounder gives the lymph system the tonic it needs; particularly useful when the weather is not conducive to going for a walk.

Just as water is essential inside our bodies, so it is outside, on our skin. The Old Testament gives rules for ritual washing, and this has kept them strong and healthy as a race throughout the centuries. It was thorough, ritual, washing that prevented the Jews from catching the plague which killed millions in the fifteenth century.

We read in John 9:7 about the man who was waiting to be healed in the waters of the Pool of Siloam, and there are spa's around the world where the waters are supposed to be particularly healing. The Dead Sea is one of the best, because the minerals are so concentrated.

A long hot soak in the bath is very relaxing and therapeutic at the end of a tiring day, especially if one puts some natural minerals in the water. Anyone who has bathed in the Dead Sea knows the extraordinary benefits of these minerals for general aches and pains, arthritis, psoriasis, asthma and eczema. I use the minerals which I bring back from the Holy Land each time I visit, and failing that I have found that Epsom salts ease aches and pains, and also purify the body.

Body wraps are a great way to lose cellulite caused by a toxic diet, and these can be done at home very inexpensively. All that is needed is a good supply of long, thick crepe bandages, saturated in bowl filled with very hot water and Epsom Salts. These hot wet bandages are wound firmly around the body in any affected area, fixed with safety pins. Then the bandages are water proofed by winding plastic bags over the top. Long transparent plastic bags from the dry cleaners are ideal. Sellotape these together to avoid the bandages leaking. Relax and keep warm with blankets and within an hour count the inches lost!

This treatment is followed with a good scrub in the shower, so all the shed toxins are washed away. Showering is so much more cleansing than wallowing in a bath, and after a hot evening bath it is a good idea to finish with a tepid shower both to cleanse and to stimulate the circulation. After towelling dry it is a good time to anoint with aromatherapy oil, lavender oil being perfect for a good night's sleep, and lemon oil invigorating in the morning.

The most efficient way to detox is a coffee enema. This can be done nightly with coffee made from body temperature distilled water, before the bath. It only takes ten minutes to do and ensures the body is clean inside as well as outside. People who are battling arthritis or cancer find tremendous pain relief from this water treatment. All that is required is a home enema kit, the privacy and peace of a locked bathroom, and a sunbed to lie on, covered with plastic sheet for protection. You lie down and insert the soft pliable rubber enema tube several inches into the rectum, and slowly and gently run the contents of the holder into the intestine.

Pause to allow any premature bowel contractions to subside. Panting will stop the desire to expel the water. When the entire amount has been absorbed into the intestine gently massage the abdomen to allow the water to cleanse the bowel. After a few moments turn onto the right side and continue to massage, and then the left side. When the whole area has been cleansed gently rise and release all the toxins and flush them away. The relief and feeling of invigoration and well being is worth the effort.

This is the one time that coffee is permitted and even encouraged as you de-toxify the body. There is only one place to take coffee, and it is not through the mouth! The very toxicity and diuretic effect of coffee makes it an excellent medium for leaching all the toxins out of the 27 feet of intestines adults have. It is particularly good when it reaches high into the gut and actually hits the liver. Most of our toxins are trapped in the liver, and the diuretic action of the coffee releases them most efficiently.

The amount of putrid gunk which has collected after a life time of eating animal protein and dairy products is quite horrific. The lining of the gut becomes lined so that the actual tube that food passes through is dramatically narrowed. Hence the bloated stomachs we tend to have in middle age!

Washing this gunk out is the quickest way to release the toxins and feel fresh again. The weight loss is apparent after several treatments, and once one has got into the practice one feels quite unclean without this detoxification. Once one has done several coffee enemas, plain distilled water may be used. Many people find adding a few drops of peppermint oil to the enema is good for digestion.

As well as water enemas for the bowel, most women are accustomed to vaginal douching with water with a special, bulb shaped douche. Two or three drops of Citricidal grape seed extract diluted in the warm distilled water will prevent urinary infections and thrush in this area.

A few drops of grape seed extract are also wonderful for normal hand washing through the day. Many germs are picked up from the myriad of things we touch daily, and it is really important to keep a soft nail brush in each basin in the house and in a plastic bag in the handbag so one can clean under the nails every time the hands are washed.

There is so much about water in the Bible. From the time that God flooded the earth, drowning the wicked, so that only the faithful Noah and his family survived, water has been used to wash away sin. The stunningly beautiful colours of the rainbow are a joyful reminder of that fresh start promised by God, shown in the sunshine and fresh fragrance that follows cleansing rain.

No wonder God ordains a believer's baptism in water. What a powerful moment it is to be totally immersed in the Jordan in the Holy Land, and rise out of the waters to a new life in Christ. Although I had been baptised as a baby and confirmed at fourteen, I wanted to receive a biblical believer's baptism. I have been baptised in the Jordan twice by Pastors Benny Hinn and Steve Hill, for fire on my ministry. I emerged from the water a new creature in Christ Jesus, and recommend the experience to all Christians. It is biblical. We should come to Christ, repent of our sins and then get baptised.

Babies are brought to infant baptism involuntarily, which is not biblical. Because it was traditional, I had been baptised as an infant, and had brought my three babies for infant baptism in church. But when I began to study my Bible, I realised that that is not what Jesus ordained. The Bible makes it quite clear that we have to repent and be baptised, as a believer. Then it has meaning. Following this Biblical directive, many babies are now brought to church for a dedication, as Jesus was, as a baby, in the temple.

The actual baptism should be a much more significant event later in life, as when Jesus himself was baptised in water and the Holy Spirit. Our Confirmation in the Protestant Church, First Communion in the Catholic Church, and Bar Mitzvah in the Jewish tradition are traditionally held at a much better time, when meaningful commitment can be made.

One of the most important teachings in the Bible is about Jesus washing his disciples' feet before the last supper. After He had done so, He then asked them if they understood the meaning of what He had done. He told them that they must wash each other's feet. We too, must serve others and "wash their feet." In this way, as we serve others with a servant heart, Jesus says we will be blessed ourselves. We need to be washed and to wash others with the Living Water of the Word, and to reveal it in our lives. And we need constant contact with the Living Water, the Word of God, in order to do this. The world, the flesh and the devil are ever present, seducing us to conform to the world. But as James 4:7 says *"Submit yourselves then, to God. Resist the devil and he will flee"*

As we read at the beginning of this chapter, God tells us through Deuteronomy 15, that the Children of Israel camped near the twelve springs at Elim. In order to stay healthy we need to stay near the Jesus, the Word of God, to provide Living Water.

As James, one of the half brothers of Jesus, says in his book, James 3:11
"Can both fresh water and salt water flow from the same spring? My brothers, can a fig–tree bear olives, or a grapevine bear figs? Neither can a salt spring produce fresh water."

We cannot be double minded, James says in James 1:6, *"like a wave of the sea, blown and tossed by the wind."*

In order to sweeten our lives we need to live by fresh, sweet, Living Water which we can drink. And just as the pure living water of the Word sweetens our minds and spirits, this pure living water is the most healing thing we can put into our bodies. Pure water, and the juice of vegetables and fruits, full of water distilled naturally by the plant, is the answer to building perfect, healthy bodies. In the next chapter we see how high water content food and pure living enzymes should be the basis of our food.

Chapter Seven

Living Food - release from the bondage of dead food!

If we want slim and healthy bodies, boundless energy, joyful enthusiasm and long life, we need to study God's Word on our diet. God's Word is very clear regarding our food. Immediately after God creates us, He gives us the perfect, high water content diet in Genesis 1:29 and 30:

"I give you every seed-bearing plant on the face of the whole earth and every tree that has fruit with seed in it. They will be yours for food. And to all the beasts of the earth and all the birds of the air and all the creatures that move on the ground – everything that has the breath of life in it – I give every green plant for food."

So many diets have been invented in the last few decades, as many people have got sicker and more obese. Most people are on some kind of diet, and most people fail miserably. Even if they lose weight from not eating so much, they get sick of the diet and sick ON the diet.

It's always the same when we try to go our own way out of stubbornness and ignorance. As Hosea 4:6 says *"My people die for lack of knowledge."* We only have to look in the first book of the Bible to find the perfect food plan!

This diet of living enzymes contained in vegetables, fruits, nuts and seed is the only one that provides all the building blocks our cells must have. When we revert to God's Word, amazing healings are happening from over one hundred and seventy different diseases, including cancer, arthritis, diabetes and heart disease. These are the degenerative diseases that are killing us prematurely, at increasingly younger ages in the western world.

This Genesis life plan directed by God is the diet that has healed me! It represents liberation from bondage to food addictions and toxins. It is the most delicious food I have ever tasted, and I am never hungry for anything else. I am living on this nutritious, God ordained food for the rest of my life.

How many times have we eaten a steak and chips or cakes and ice cream only to be disappointed? How many times have we indulged in a chocolate bar and then felt despair? They did not taste as good as we thought they were going to, and afterwards we not only feel fat but we feel guilty. And we also feel foolish. We have allowed ourselves to be duped again!

In an evil world where half the people are dying of starvation and the other half dying of overindulgence, the message has never been more salient. God's food is inexpensive and easy to produce. We could eradicate starvation within days if the western world disciplined themselves to eat God's food only, and used the money they saved on empty, toxic and processed foods, to provide water for the poor to grow these basic crops. That is what God intended us to do, and what Jesus actually told us to do. In Matthew 25:35-40, he says that when we feed the hungry, we have done it to him. In doing so, the overindulged would regain their health!

We are clearly to live on vegetables, plants, fruit, seeds, and green plants. And we are to eat them raw. This is the fastest, most delicious and convenient food in the world!

What a joy to wake to a glass of purifying green barley shoot juice followed by a golden juice of carrot, apple, pineapple and strawberry, to feel the goodness seeping into the body like a transfusion of energy. On cool mornings I follow the juices with hot water, honey and lemon, with a little infused ginger to ginger me up. If I am going to be specially active, or have to miss lunch, I might follow the juices with a crunchy muesli made of fresh flaked almonds, linseeds, pumpkin seeds, apples, raisins, and other fruit, soaked in fresh apple juice, infinitely nicer than milk which is acid, congesting and clogs the body!

Solomon says in the Song of Solomon 2:5 "Strengthen me with raisins, refresh me with apples" – a good way to start the morning! Mid morning I would have another glass of juice, and a bunch of grapes or a banana, which is high in potassium. Lunch would be a fresh tomato juice, hot or cold homemade vegetable soup according to the weather, followed by a crisp green salad with lots of colours. I would add raw slices of organic tomatoes, green, orange or yellow peppers, cucumber, celery and pineapple chunks, sprouts, fresh coleslaw, and crunchy fresh nuts and topped with a delicious avocado or honey, mustard and olive oil dressing.

For an afternoon snack another glass of carrot, apple or pineapple juice, or perhaps an almond smoothie with strawberries or raspberries or kiwi fruit on top. Blend the almonds and water to a smooth cream, and top the smoothie with raspberries or halved strawberries and a few almonds.

Supper would be a glass of fresh carrot and tomato juice or grape juice, followed by an avocado salad with green leaves, cucumber, celery and pineapple, or gorgeous lightly steamed vegetables in butter, or baked potato with avocado or salsa sauce, or maybe brown rice with onions and garlic, garden peas and almonds. Try a banana, honey or raisin dessert or simply a few dates, and finish with a hot drink of pure water, lemon and honey.

This diet will have given us the living enzymes we need for super energy, and the cell building blocks necessary to heal. And unlike the SAD (Standard American Diet, or stupid addictive diet) we will not have had any toxins or allergens from animal protein, wheat, alcohol, sugar or dairy foods.

For generations we have been indoctrinated by the powerful, government backed food industry that we need protein in animal products, meat, poultry and fish. Remember the ads "Drinka pinta milka day" – WHO **REALLY** WANTS TO SUCKLE A COW? and "Go to work on an egg!" Do you **REALLY** WANT TO EAT AN EMBRYO? Little have we realised that governments and the food industry work together for their mutual benefit. They get richer and we get sicker! We remember how the American government still backs the tobacco industry, from which it derives taxes, all the while putting a warning on the package.

We have to learn to take responsibility for our own health!
Psalm 118:8, in the very heart of the Bible, says *"It is better to take refuge in the Lord than to trust in man."*

People seeking to lose weight may have tried many diets designed by man, but most have failed or become ill simply because their bodies are not designed to follow those diets. They have lost weight by giving up carbohydrates, but have become sick and found life intolerable because they are still deficient in living enzymes. God's diet is the only one that gives those in correct proportions. Others have tried high protein diets but have become very ill suffering from constipation and arthritis, as the acid levels build up in the body. Diets that ban fruit and vegetables are disastrous to the body.

Juicy fruits like pineapple, lemons, oranges, pears, grapefruits, apricots, papayas, kiwis, peaches and blueberries all help to digest protein. As we remember from our meat eating days, apple has always been eaten with pork to aid digestion. Sugary, starchy fruits like bananas, raisons and dates aid the digestion of carbohydrates.

Fruit must always be eaten on an empty stomach as it is digested quickly. If we eat fruit after carbohydrates and protein, the fruit waits and ferments while the cooked foods are being digested. This is why we should always start meals with juice, vegetables or fruit.

Because some fruit juices contain a lot of fructose, a natural sugar, they may be watered down with pure water. When juicing vegetables, it is a good idea to add apple juice to lighten them.

The truth about protein is that it is made up of twenty three amino acids. Our bodies already produce fifteen of them, and the other eight are derived from fruit, vegetables, nuts and whole grains like natural, unrefined brown rice, barley and rye.

Any argument that we need protein is confounded by the immense strength and power of huge animals like cattle, horses, even elephants, which are all grass eaters. Humans simply do not have the short straight gut, the tearing teeth and the huge amounts of hydrochloric acid needed to consume animal flesh. Anyone who tells us we need animal protein is simply misinformed. We are our healthiest on a vegetarian diet.

Dave Scott has won the Iron man Triathlon World Championships three times, Sixto Linares holds the world record for the 24 hour triathlon, swimming 4.8 miles, cycling 186 miles and running 52.2 miles. Paavo Nuni has won twenty world records in distance running and nine Olympic medals. These events require huge stamina and strength. All these athletes are vegetarians!

Huge endurance is required, and the right nutrition is absolutely vital. It used to be thought best for endurance athletes to stock up on high carbohydrate intake the evening before a race. But pasta is paste and paste is not the best thing to put into your intestines if you want to have energy. We should remember that the adult human intestine measures twenty seven feet and is convoluted and compressed in the abdomen. Protein putrifies and carbohydrate ferments in the warm, dark, folds, and the gut becomes lined with toxic waste, only permitting a small amount of food to be assimilated and to pass through. Parasites from animal flesh thrive and breed in this area.

The only foods to energise and cleanse the body are the living enzymes found in raw vegetables and fruit, seeds, nuts and green plants. This is living food, which has been cleansed, as the water content has been distilled by the plant, nature's own refinery. The body cannot assimilate minerals in an inorganic form, so most manufactured supplements pass straight through the body, possibly even causing kidney stones. Plants, however, convert these inorganic minerals by photosynthesis, into the organic, living minerals we need. God's perfect laboratory.

Having established that we need to eat a lot of raw food, the next step is to find the easiest way to digest this high fibre food. It takes a lot of energy to digest raw food, and the best way to assimilate this goodness, particularly when health is already compromised, is to juice it with a special electric juicer.

The juice you will make yourself from fresh fruit and vegetables you have selected and cleaned yourself, is guaranteed to be delicious, pure, cleansing, and healing. It contains all the natural goodness necessary to keep us fit.

Very few people realise that when we heat food to over 107 degrees to cook it, we lose all the living enzymes. Therefore all pasteurised, bottled, tinned and packaged food, including juice, has lost its goodness as it was processed. For centuries now, our ancestors have ignored God's health instructions and many in western society have become obese, leading to sickness.

One in three of us dies prematurely of heart disease, and another one in three of us now dies of cancer at increasingly young ages. Diabetes rates are the highest ever, affecting many young people. One third of our young men and women are infertile.

After sin came into the world, God despaired of man, and sent the flood to destroy all mankind. Only the faithful Noah and his family survived and they had to eat animals until the fruit and vegetables grew again. In Genesis 9:3 God now says:

"Everything that lives and moves will be food for you. I now give you everything. But you must not eat meat that has its lifeblood still in it. And for your lifeblood I will surely demand an accounting, I will demand an accounting from every animal. And from each man too I will demand an accounting for the life of his fellow man."

So we can now eat anything apart from red meat! Or can we? God says that we are now accountable for our actions. We have free choice as Adam and Eve did in Genesis 2, but we will suffer the consequences of bad choice.

There was no meat in that original diet! In fact, it was not until some one thousand, seven hundred years after God gave mankind the Genesis 1:29 diet, a pure, raw, vegan diet, that man first consumed the flesh of an animal. And that was apparently only for survival purposes because the flood had destroyed most plant life.

Only the odd olive tree remained, so that the dove could bring the leaf to Noah.

If you have ever visited a factory farm, a blood-spattered abattoir or seen fish gasping on the end of a fishing line, hanging from a cruel metal hook in its mouth, or caught in a net, any compassionate person is repelled at the cruelty. There is no avoiding the issue, these animals suffer appallingly and die in great fear. We know instinctively this is not what God ordained. Animal sacrifice in the Old Testament was done quickly and expertly by slitting the animal's throat, but Jesus came to die as the ultimate paschal lamb so that it was not necessary to sacrifice the temple lambs any more.

We are accountable for every animal and this very strong moral argument is added to the weight of God's Word in Genesis 1:29 and 30. Animals are not supposed to have to live constrictive lives and die horrible deaths in order that we should gorge on their flesh.

Jesus would not have eaten much meat. He probably only ate a small portion of well roast lamb at Jewish feasts like Passover, or celebratory feasts such as weddings. The meat never contained blood and was well cooked.

We store toxins in the liver and in our fat cells, as do animals. Therefore, an animal's liver is about the most toxic thing we can eat. Chicken is no better, the birds are fed steroids and antibiotics. They are plumped up for supermarkets with high doses of oestrogen, which leads to prostate cancer in men and breast and ovarian cancer in women.

Roast lamb was the meat of choice, and in those days the lambs were fed on grass, they were leaner and healthier, and they had not been fed the hormones and antibiotics that meat contains today.

We can always see God's judgement in the stories of the Bible. Whereas man lived to great ages in the Old Testament, Methuselah being the oldest at nine hundred and sixty nine, things have gone very wrong. Once sin and disobedience entered the world, and our diet changed to including animal protein, our life span reduced dramatically to 120 years.

In Genesis 6:3, God says
"My Spirit will not contend with man for ever. For he is mortal, his days will be a hundred and twenty years."

When we get to David's time, our span has shortened still further. Psalm 90:10 says
"The length of our days is seventy years –
Or eighty, if we have the strength;
Yet their span is but trouble and sorrow
For they quickly pass, and we fly away.

It is a salutary and disturbing fact that the average doctor today only lives to fifty two, which surely tells us something. If the people we pay to be our health advisors are so unhealthy, surely it is time we sought better advice! The best advice we can seek is always God's Word. So why are we so stupid as to ignore it? What a disaster that we do not obey His instructions. Hosea 4:2 says *"My people die for lack of knowledge"* and this is so true. Generations of people have been dying because they have not obeyed God's Word in Genesis 1:29 and 30.

Since I have been healed on this diet, I have now discovered that over two million other people are actually following God's dietary rules. They are living on the raw vegetables and fruits, seeds and green plants of the Genesis Diet, and they are remaining active to a good age and not dying prematurely of heart disease, cancer and diabetes. Neither are they barren, like one third of our western society.

Hippocrates, a physician who lived in the fifth century before Jesus Christ, is known as the "Father of Medicine." Hippocrates is legendary for saying "Let food be your medicine and medicine your food." He also said that our food should be eaten in the condition it is found in nature. That means uncooked!

This indicates that wheat and barley should be consumed raw, as in wheat and barley grass. Jesus' disciples ate raw grains as we read in Matthew 12:1. As we saw earlier, in chapter three, the most nutritious green plant in the world has been found to be barley grass juice. Wheat grass juice used to be popular, but as we know, wheat is the cause of many allergies. Barley grass is infinitely better.

Some people pray over their food and think this will purify it. Exodus 23:25 says *"Worship the Lord your God, and his blessing will be on your food and your water"...* But we cannot eat toxic food and pray that God will bless it. God has given clear directives in His Word as to what we should be eating, and 20th and 21st century food is far from what He intended.

The healthiest diet in the world is pure water, vegetable and fruit juice, nuts, seeds and green plant. When we eat this food, we are never hungry. Our body is receiving the pure living enzymes it needs and we lose all cravings for toxic food.

As children we used to make paste from flour and water. It stuck things hard and fast! And that is exactly what happens when we eat flour based foods, washed down with liquid! The glutinous mass clogs our digestive system. When we eat bread, cakes and biscuits – anything made with flour – we have actually eaten paste!

Dairy produce is also very unhealthy. We have eaten glue when we drink clogging dairy produce, which is very mucous forming. No other living creatures drink milk except when they suckle their mothers, and neither should we! Milk, like wheat, is responsible for most of the allergies we have. One in five children in the western world now has asthma! Many asthmatics are completely healed when they eliminate dairy and wheat from their diets.

The milk drunk in biblical times was mainly goats and sheep's milk, which is much more digestible. The term *"a land flowing with milk and honey"* did not describe dairy farming as we know it, as much as it illustrated a peaceful land where sheep could graze unafraid and wild flowers could grow so that bees could make honey.

What a joy it is to be rid of food allergies and food cravings. What a joy to have freedom from toxins! We will never again be hungry, or addicted to harmful caffeine, salt, sugar, dairy products, animal proteins and cooked foods. Once the body is getting the living enzymes it craves, we can live healthily to a ripe old age on this wonderful living food.

The Bible goes on to describe some other healthy foods in Deuteronomy 8:8. I have found that these, in their natural state, as God intended, are great foods to add occasionally, once the body has healed from sickness, and one wants a little diversity.

"For the Lord thy God brings thee in a good land,
a land of brooks of water, of fountains and
depths that spring out of valleys and hills,
A land of wheat and barley
And vines and fig trees and pomegranates,
A land of olive oil and honey."

The unleavened bread of the Holy Land is much healthier than the bread we have in the west. Western bread contains yeast which feeds candida infections, which can then spread throughout the body.

Moreover, western bread has lost all its nutrients. All wheat germ is removed from the flour because it clogs up bread making machinery and bran is also removed because it leaves brown flecks in the flour. Then the flour is bleached with chemical to make white, totally empty, bread. Petro-chemical "vitamins" are then added to make the bread "enriched with vitamins". Enriched with poison! If we soak white bread in water we find it reduced to a glutinous mess. That is what we have been putting in our bodies! Brown bread, which we think is healthier, is often exactly the same thing, but with added colouring.

Essene bread, eaten by the Essenes who lived in caves at Qumran near the Dead Sea, is the healthiest bread we can eat. It is made from sprouted seeds, walnuts, almonds, dates, apples, olive oil and parsley. It is wheat and dairy free, low in fats, cholesterol, sodium and saturates and high in fibre. The recipe for Essene bread may be found in the recipe chapter of this book.

If you have no time to bake Essene bread, Dr Karg´s little organic whole grain crisp breads with sunflower seeds, sesame seeds, pumpkin seeds and linseeds are an excellent and convenient alternative. They are good topped with blended avocado as a savoury, and also with honey for breakfast.

But for ease of assimilation, when on the Genesis diet, we are best to drink barley grass (green plant). A Japanese research pharmacologist, Dr. Yoshilde Hagiwara, became seriously ill due to handling mercury in his laboratory. None of the medicines his firm made could heal him, so he turned his factory over to researching for the best source of green plant. It was discovered that tender young barley shoots grown high up in unpolluted mountain regions contained more vitamins, minerals, proteins, chlorophyll and enzymes than any other. He found a way to stabilise the barley grass so that it could be packaged and distributed without losing its nutrients. Dr. Hagiwara recovered his health with barley grass, the "green plant" God tells us to eat, and this powder is now sold worldwide. It is reconstituted with distilled water, and mixed by shaking in a 33cl glass bottle. It is good to drink two or three green barley juices each day.

The vine, of course, is very biblical, and was used by Jesus in many of his parables. Both grapes and wine are an important part of biblical teaching. Jesus said *"I am the vine and you are the branches"* in John 15:5. Jesus also offered the cup of red wine, symbolising his blood, at the Last Supper. He said in Luke 22:19 *"when you drink it, do this in remembrance of me."*

However, the wine of biblical times was not as strong as the wine we drink today. The new wine that Jesus drank was only slightly alcoholic. Wine is mentioned by Paul in his first letter to Timothy 5:23. He recommends that Timothy should *"take a little wine for the sake of your stomach"* as it disinfects impure water. In his letter to the Ephesians 5:18, however, he warns *"do not get drunk on wine for that is debauchery!"*

Noah was the first man to grow wine, as we see in Genesis 9:20, and sadly also the first man in the Bible to be intoxicated. His sons had to cover up his nakedness and it led to the cursing of his youngest son.

91

Natural grape juice is far healthier. It is a powerful anti-inflammatory. It also contains just as many antioxidants and polyphenols without the harmful yeasts caused by fermentation and additives that are found in wine. Very often it is the tannin in the casks that the wine is matured in, that cause allergy. Some people are allergic to the meta-bisulphates used in modern processing of wine, and feel ill and may start sneezing at the first sip!

Grape seeds are rich in Vitamin B 17, and people have been cured of cancer on the "Grape Diet", eating only grapes with seeds. However this does not provide the other fruits, vegetables and green plant which are also necessary for good health.

When liquidised, grape seeds are a powerful antiseptic, available over the counter, called Citricidal. Grapes are useful to snack on when coming off chocolate. They are handy to nibble and contain antioxidants and polyphenols as well as a natural sugar, fructose, rather than the unhealthy caffeine, milk and manufactured sucrose sugar of chocolate.

Figs are particularly healing, both internally and externally. They contain benzaldehyde, which has anti-cancer and anti-tumoral properties. In 2 Kings 20:1-11, King Hezekiah was healed of his life-threatening disease by putting fig poultice on his body. People today still crush figs and then place them on tumours to disperse them. Figs are very cleansing to the digestive system, as we may recall from being given Syrup of Figs as children!

Pomegranates are known as "the royal fruit", and their juice is very high in anti-oxidants. It is also an effective anti-inflammatory. Pomegranate juice is said to help the fight against Alzheimer's Disease, heart disease, and arthritis. It has a high sugar content, however, so should be diluted with carrot, celery or cucumber juice. Olives have been a nutritious food, easy to pick and eat. Olive oil has always been a precious commodity, and is used for anointing spiritually and also in aromatherapy. It is believed that spiritual properties can be absorbed, just as the essential oils are physically absorbed by the skin.

In the Holy Land today we still see olives being harvested by farming families. The boys climb up and shake and beat the trees with sticks to dislodge the ripe olives, and the girls collect the harvest in special sheets they have spread under the trees.

Donkeys used to turn the heavy stone mills. Today mechanical presses are used, but the olives must still be crushed within 24 hours, as they spoil very quickly. Extra virgin olive oil, the finest, must be cold pressed, with no chemicals or hot water added during the process. The acidity level must be lower than one percent, and the oil must have an excellent flavour and aroma. No wonder it is so expensive.

Olive oil is thought, however, to be very health giving. As a mono-saturated fatty acid it doesn't have the same cholesterol-raising effect of saturated fats, and is a good source of anti-oxidants. It is also said to prevent stickiness in the blood.

Olive oil is best taken as a salad dressing, mixed with honey and a little mustard. There is an olive oil cure for gall stones in which you mix four ounces of olive oil with four ounces of freshly squeezed lemon juice, which you drink before going to bed. You lay on your right side with a heated pad underneath you. All sludge and small gall stones will be flushed out of the gall bladder in the night, and will be expelled the next day.

Honey is also a biblical food. Psalm 119:103 says that God's words are *"sweeter than honey to my mouth."* Honey is liquid gold, full of minerals and antioxidants, and has antiseptic properties, particularly when raw and dark. We should use it instead of sugar. It is especially good as an energising drink, when stirred into hot water with a squeeze of lemon.

These biblical directives on food are corroborated by the most up to date, serious research doctors. An American heart doctor called T. Colin Campbell, who has just brought out his book "The China Study," has spent forty years researching into the relationship of diet to disease. He says **"even small intakes of animal foods, meat, eggs and milk, are associated with significant increases of chronic degenerative disease. Change your diet and**

dramatically reduce your risk of cancer, heart disease, diabetes and obesity."

Many people think they can do God's diet half heartedly. They toy with juices in the morning and then lapse during the day. But the benefits elude them. Galatians 6:7 says *"Do not be deceived. God cannot be mocked. A man reaps what he sows."* The only way this diet will heal you is to go on it wholeheartedly.

The Lord intends us to live healthy, fruitful lives. Jesus said in John 10:10 *"I have come to give you life, and life in all abundance."* That means serving Him, and living in His blessing. We cannot do that if we are disobedient to his Word.

It is time that we brought health back into the Church. Too many Christians are sick because of their ignorance of God's health directives and disobedience to God's dietary laws. As Romans 10:14 says *"How can they hear without someone telling them".* What better witness than one who has been healed! As we preach salvation, so we should preach abundant, healthy life, now while we are God's temple on earth.

Paul says in 1 Corinthians 3:16
"Do you not know, have you not heard, that you yourselves are God's temple and that God's Spirit lives in you? If anyone destroys God's temple, God will destroy him; for God's temple is sacred and you are that temple"

We need to return to the Living Food God ordained for us to eat, rather than the dead food we have become accustomed to. Jesus says in John 8:32 *"You will know the truth and the truth will set you free!"* Free from sin, from sickness and overweight, unhealthy bodies! Praise God!

Chapter 8

The skin, our covering

He will cover you with His feathers
And under his wings you will find refuge.
Psalm 91:4

Many of us do not appreciate that our skin, our covering, is the body's largest organ, and comprises 20-30% of our body weight.

Each square centimetre has six million cells, 5000 sensory points and 100 sweat glands. Our skin is constantly changing and by the end of each month has been completely regenerated. So we need to exfoliate the old cells and encourage healthy new ones. Skin brushing has been used for thousands of years, and really rejuvenates our covering. The skin should be brushed every morning to slough off the toxins and dead skin cells shed in the night, and it also helps to disperse cellulite on the arms, tummy and thighs. Follow this with a shower, and finish by anointing all over with a protective cover of oil.

Anointing ourselves morning and evening gives us a fragrant covering. There is no need to buy expensive aromatherapy oils when one can make one's own. I use almond oil as a base, pouring a teaspoon into the palm of my left hand, and adding a few drops of essential oils for specific purposes. Lemon is delightful for invigorating and freshening after the morning shower, lavender calms at night, and the wonderful Australian melaleuca, or tea tree oil, heals and purifies the skin.

Like Esther in the Bible, who spent a year of preparation saturating her body with precious essences for her night with the King, and became his queen, we need to smell and feel good! What a glorious way to start your day, anointed with *"the oil of gladness"* as the Bible says in Psalm 45:7.

We remember how Jesus praised Mary of Bethany when she anointed him with the costly oil in the alabaster box. Aromatherapy oil is a very special gift. I often give it as a Christmas present, reminding people of Jesus, and starting them, perhaps, on a wonderful, healthy New Year routine.

Our skin represents the first line of defence against dehydration, infection, injuries and temperature extremes. Our underarm temperature should remain at 98.6 degrees, and if this rises or falls by five or six degrees, our life is actually in danger.

Our skin can also, to a degree, detoxify harmful external substances, just as the liver detoxifies internally. However, the skin does not have an ability to filter everything it comes in contact with. It acts like a sponge, taking in everything it encounters and unable to detoxify everything. Therefore we should be cautious about the cosmetics, shampoos and insect repellents we use. By looking on the internet we can find many natural products to replace chemical ones. Toothpaste for instance contains toxins. It can be replaced by baking soda flavoured with essential oil of peppermint.

We know that the skin on the face and hands is the most visible and needs the most protection from sun and wind. The skin should be plumped up, moist and vibrant, and whether it is dry, oily or sensitive, it needs to be hydrated regularly, particularly where sunlight is strong.

As we have already seen, it is essential to drink enough water to hydrate the body, including the skin. It also helps to hydrate the face by spraying a film of water on it before applying a protective film of almond oil, sun protection and make up.

Oily skin is the bane of many of our lives when we are young, but does have its benefits as we age. It will look youthful longer, especially if we use steam and natural masks.

Sensitive skin is still a normal, dry or oily skin. It is sensitive to chemicals and alcohol, oils, and fragrances, and usually benefits from natural products such as almond oil. Dr. Valnet produces a healing oil made from apricot kernels which is of course rich in B17. http://bio.plus.free.fr.Huiles essentielles Dr. Valnet.

It is also good to inhale some healthy oils to clear the respiratory system. You can make your own portable inhaler by sterilising and reusing a small plastic airtight container such as a photographic film protector. When clean and dry, fill the container with some tissue. Then sprinkle essential oils like cinnamon, clove and thyme onto the tissue and warm the container in the hands. It makes a useful little personal inhaler, perfect for travelling and in the handbag. Great to use when in crowded places like airports and planes!

For a more substantial inhaler, Vicks make a simple 15 cm high plastic screw top one, the hot water and essential oil is poured into an inner non-spillable container for safety.

Aloe vera, quoted in the Song of Solomon 4:13, has wonderful healing properties. It stops the burning and pain of a sore throat, irritation in the skin, and soothes sunburn and all other burns. It's a good idea to keep an aloe plant on the kitchen window sill.

The aloe gel also stops digestive pain and the burning of cystitis. It is interesting that a great deal of award winning research is being done on the aloe which has now become the science of glyco-nutrients. It has been found that Ambrotose, made by Mannatech, a powder containing eight essential poly-saccharides including aloe, has anti-tumoral and immune building properties. www.manatech.com.

Candida albicans is a skin infection which afflicts many of us. There are an estimated 100,000 to 200,000 species of fungus. Of these, some 180 are capable of triggering disease in humans and animals through tissue invasion. Hippocrates and Galen were amongst the first to describe fungal and yeast infections in their patients. However it was not until the 1800's that doctors realised that it could be passed to a new born child by an infected mother.

Unfortunately the incidence of opportunistic infections by micro-organisms such as candida albicans have now become prevalent, mainly being due to the widespread and often unwarranted use of antibiotics, immuno-suppressive drugs and the introduction of surgical procedures.

Yeast infection, or candidiasis, has been called the "twentieth century disease" due to its tremendous upsurge since the discovery and introduction of sulphur drugs and mould-based antibiotics such as penicillin. Recent statistics from America indicate that one in every three people living in our Western, industrialised society is riddled with this destructive invader.

Candida albicans is highly virulent, with common sites of infestation including the kidneys (for which candida has a recognized predilection), the brain (particularly the meninges), the gastro-intestinal tract and the mitral and aortic valves of the heart.

Numerous factors are known to predispose an overgrowth of yeast, but the greatest incidences of yeast infestation occur in patients who have been treated with antibiotics and steroids. Often entry into the body is via the gastro-intestinal tract, where the organism passes across the intestinal mucosa into the bloodstream.

Even though candida albicans can be cultured from the stool of at least ninety percent of babies six to nine months old, its presence is overlooked or ignored when a patient is examined.

The fungi can mimic a number of diseases and clinical signs. These symptoms should not be ignored, because the yeast overgrowth severely damages the immune system. A compromised immune system is then unable to fight off bacterial and viral infections, leading to the taking of more harmful antibiotics which cause an even greater infestation.

To rectify the problem it is necessary to adopt God's diet in Genesis, which starves the yeast so that it cannot survive, and at the same time, to use natural anti-fungal elements. It is also critical to employ natural products rather than antibiotics, so as not to destroy the friendly bacteria in the gastro-intestinal tract that protect the body from yeast overgrowth.

In addition to infection, candida has been known to cause allergic reaction in humans. It has been said that fungus is the most complex infectious agent studied. This is based on findings that one strain of the yeast is capable of releasing seventy-nine different toxic substances into the bloodstream.

Symptoms of colonization are widespread and depend on where the organisms are sited and where their toxins are collecting. Sites of invasion include the internal vital organs including the intestines and the mitral and aortic valves of the heart; the armpits, groin, sub-mammary fold, toe clefts, nails and nail folds, gums, vagina, testes, and the nappy area in babies.

Factors that predispose to candidiasis include the Western diet, which is loaded with sugars of many varieties. Sugar is candida's favourite nutrient. Other candidiasis forming foods are ferments such as beer and champagne, soy sauce and vinegar, mould-injected foods like Brie, Camembert, and blue cheeses.

Endocrine disorders, drug addiction, severe stress, trauma such as burns and malignancies also add to candidiasis, as does the alteration of the necessary flora of the gastro-intestinal tract or suppression of the natural immunity of the body through the indiscriminate use of antibiotics, oral contraceptives, anti-depressant drugs, corticosteroids and cytotoxic drugs.

Infestation can be manifested in a range of symptoms including, but not restricted to, gastric upsets, I.B.S. (irritable bowel syndrome), bloating, intense fatigue (chronic fatigue syndrome) scalp disorders, skin complaints, headaches, depression, nasal congestion and mucous problems, ear infections, hearing problems, throat infections, swollen glands, glandular disorders, heartburn, menstrual disorders, itching, chest infections, kidney and bladder disorders, loss of libido, fluid retention, allergic reactions, weight problems, mental disorders, muscle weakness and joint pains, heart palpitations, circulation disorders, personality changes and bingeing.

Severe food cravings indicate candida albicans infestation, as this fungus forces the body to crave the very foods it needs in order to thrive and multiply. It may demand anything from sugars and hydrogenated oils to fruits and starches, and usually commands great helpings. A Vegemite or Marmite sandwich, is a classic example – comprising yeast in both the bread and the spread. Yeast craves more yeast and yeast feeds yeast. Given the right fuel, candida will multiply at an unbelievable rate, leaving the victim with the uncomfortable and often painful, but inevitable consequences.

Therefore the first and main line treatment is to starve the fungus by not feeding it with any of the food it needs and wants in order to survive. Second, the organism must be slowly destroyed by an anti-fungal agent.

Conventional medical practitioners use Nyastin, Nizoral, Griseofulvin, Canesten and Amphotericin amongst their arsenal, which actually add fuel to the fire. They cause further infestation once usage is discontinued, as they strengthen the fungus whilst they are being used. Many of them also impact negatively on the liver. Natural practitioners will prescribe tea tree oil, garlic, pau d'arco, una de gato (cat's claw) and acidophilus.

Tea tree oil is distilled from the leaves of the Melaleuca Alternifolia tree, which is indigenous to the northern coast of New South Wales in Australia. The tree possesses powerful germicidal, fungicidal, virucidal and antiseptic properties, yet it is non-toxic and non-irritating to healthy, normal tissue. These characteristics have led to its widespread acceptance and usage in first aid, dental and surgical practice.

Aborigines have known of the wonderful, medicinal properties of tea tree oil for centuries. Its aromatic extracts can and will clear chest infections, sinus and hay fever, soothe itchy skin eruptions, reduce psoriasis of the scalp, relieve vaginal thrush, prevent excessive ear wax secretion, soothe painful mouth ulcers, fight herpes attacks, alleviate sore throats and eliminate some strains of tinea and ringworm.

The value of the tea tree oil in the fight against candida albicans is inestimable. Candida sufferers will benefit greatly in adding a teaspoon of this oil to their bathwater; inhaling the vapours of steam from a few drops added to a bowl of hot water three times weekly and gargling with a solution of three drops in a glass of warm water.

Whenever candidiasis is treated, it is vital to supplement and replace the friendly bacteria in the colon with acidophilus and bifidus. Other herbal and natural supplements such as echinacea, vitamin A, yeast free vitamin B, vitamin C, vitamin E, zinc, selenium, and magnesium, Co-enzyme Q 10 and ginseng boost the body's weakened immune system and remove toxins from the blood.

A sodium sulphate flush of a tablespoon of Epsom Salts stirred into eight ounces of hot water is ideal to start the detoxification. This flush is a detoxificant for the lymphatic system and should be undertaken in conjunction with an external body programme, ideally lymph drainage massage in the hands of a trained therapist, followed up daily with an almond and tea tree oil massage after a long hot cleansing daily bath containing a few drops of tea tree oil

Upon rising, drink eight ounces of warm water to which is added one tablespoon of sodium suphate (Na_2SO_4) obtainable from chemists without a prescription as Epsom Salts. The purpose of this saline solution is not primarily to empty the bowels, which it will do anyway, but rather to draw into the intestines from every part of the body such toxic matter and body waste that may be present and eliminate it through the bowels. The saline solution acts on the toxic lymph and body waste just like a magnet attracts nails and metal filings to itself. This body waste is then drawn into the intestines and out of the body is a series of copious eliminations from the bowel, which may amount altogether to one gallon or more. This is highly effective as an arthritis cleanse.

Half an hour after taking the saline solution, start drinking the juice of three grapefruits, five oranges and two lemons, together with an equal amount of water, for quicker absorption into the body. This has an alkaline reaction on the body and also prevents dehydration, which would have otherwise occurred if nothing were done to replace the volume of toxic or acid material being eliminated.

Continue to drink the diluted juices throughout the day until finished. This should be approximately two quarts. Alternate a mixture of juice and water with plain glasses of pure water. In most cases it is necessary to fast all day for the three days, however if really hungry towards the evening, eat some oranges or grapefruit, or their juices, or have some celery juice. Supplement a capsule of acidophilus with the drinks three times a day, together with the general immune building supplements listed above.

Before going to bed, do an enema using either two cups of coffee, a quarter of a cup of apple cider vinegar and the juice of two lemons or simply a half cup of apple cider vinegar. The purpose of doing this is to remove from the bowels any waste matter that may have remained lodged there and would otherwise be re-absorbed into the system during sleep.

This process is repeated for three consecutive days. Hence, approximately three gallons of toxic lymph will have been eliminated from the body and will have been replaced by three gallons of alkaline juices. This results in speeding up the re-alkalization of the body. On the fourth day, resume the Genesis diet of raw fruit and vegetable juices. Maintain the supplementation of the acidophilus, one capsule three times a day.

Rest up during this detoxification, as the body uses its energies for a housecleaning within. Afterwards you will be rewarded with infinitely greater energy, vitality and relief from symptoms as a result of a detoxified body. It is really important to maintain the supplements so your body does not lose essential vitamins and minerals. Most people who have experienced the benefits of this detox will choose to repeat it once a week or once a month as a maintenance programme.

After the preliminary three days, a soup may be introduced made from onions and garlic gently cooked until soft, in a saucepan with pure, best quality cold pressed virgin olive oil. When the onions are gently sautéed, add organically grown seasonal vegetables, such as celery, broccoli, or cabbage, and enough pure water to make the required quantity. When the soup has simmered long enough for the vegetables to have softened, plunge in a Magic Wand electric blender and blend the soup in the saucepan. Drink the soup fresh, never use left-overs.

Drink the soup at lunch and supper times. Never go back to eating bread or any other processed foods which contain sugar or yeast, for the candida will be only too ready to re-infest the body. Continue to supplement acidophilus with every meal. This liquid only diet should be continued for at least a week to give the body a thorough cleanse, before adding other organic fruit and lightly steamed vegetables.

It is recommended to live permanently on the Genesis diet. If you have ever had candida you should never re-introduce cheeses, breads, or any food containing flour and sugar. This includes biscuits, cakes, processed foods, jams, processed sauces and any puddings made with flour or sugar.

The good news if that after a few weeks, as the candidiasis is brought under control, all addiction to noxious foods disappears. No longer do we crave sugar or alcohol, which may contain yeast, sugar, tannin, rennin and metabisulphites, all of which are allergens and cause candida. As the blood sugar regains an even keel, we will no longer be drawn to caffeine as in tea, coffee or chocolate, or indeed meat, bread, sugar, dairy, and other foods we used to crave.

The benefits of feeling well again, having more vitality than we have had for years, the freedom from pain, bloating and cellulite, and our restored slim figures will far outweigh the dubious pleasure of the taste of these foods which have proved to act as destructive allergens in our bodies. The Genesis diet will heal us and keep us free from all toxins. At last we are free! Thank God for His amazing diet!

The skin takes on a clarity and glow that it has not had since childhood, dark circles under the eyes disappear, psoriasis and eczema are healed, and one looks ten years younger! Doctors say psoriasis cannot be healed, but like asthma, adhering faithfully to the God-ordained Genesis Diet will eventually bring about the cure!

Naaman, the proud and sceptical army commander in 2 Kings 5:10 was told to *"Go, wash yourself seven times in the Jordan, and your flesh will be restored and you will be cleansed"*. He was so stubborn and full of pride that for some time he refused. But when he eventually did what he was told in obedience and humility, he was healed and his flesh *"became clean like that of a young boy."*

We need to immerse ourselves in the Word of God, which is our covering, become obedient, and we, too shall be healed.

Chapter Nine

Dry bones come to life!

Ezekiel 37:4-5 " Dry bones, hear the Word of the Lord! This is what the Sovereign Lord says to these bones: I will make breath enter you, and you will come to life! Then you will know I am the Lord."

Arthritis is the cause of more on-going suffering than most other diseases because it may start when an individual is quite young and continue to get worse throughout a long life time. Nine out of ten people over the age of sixty have arthritis to some degree. For some it is a daily torture and can even be life threatening; for most it means living with pain and stiffness. Many people now develop osteoporosis.

The good news is that arthritis and osteoporosis are not an inevitable consequence of ageing. By learning how and why they occur in the body, one can prevent them progressing, and also eliminate the pain and inflammation by drug-free methods.

Arthritis can be caused by the body having to carry around too much weight. The strain on hip and knee joints is just too much to carry, and the joints and eventually bones break down. Sugar, dairy produce and animal protein destroy bone because the acid they make in the body causes it to leach goodness from bone marrow, instead of building it up. The Genesis lifestyle will heal arthritis and joint, ligament and muscle pain in two ways.

Firstly it provides the living enzymes which create the building blocks the cells need to create healthy bones, muscles, ligaments and tendons.

Because farm land has been depleted of minerals through intensive farming methods, we have for several generations eaten food practically devoid of minerals.

In our impatience and greed we have ignored God's directive to rest the land every seven years.

Leviticus 25:1-6 "The Lord said to Moses on Mount Sinai: Speak to the Israelites and say to them "When you enter the land I am going to give you, the land itself must observe a sabbath to the Lord. For six years sow your fields, and for six years prune your vineyards and gather their crops. But in the seventh year the land is to have a sabbath of rest, a sabbath to the Lord. Do not sow your fields or prune your vineyards. Do not reap what grows of itself or harvest the grapes of your untended vines. Whatever the land yields during the sabbath year will be food for you."

Because we have disobeyed God's Word and not rested the land every seventh year, soil has become depleted, and our health has suffered as we are no longer getting the minerals God intended us to have and which are essential for our health.

Compounding this disaster, governments and the food industry giants have now given farmers directives to add chemicals to the soil. These chemicals are damaging, and some have been proved to be carcinogenic. As well as damaging the soil, our water supply is contaminated as the chemicals gradually seep through to our national reservoirs or wells with rainwater.

We cannot put all the blame on others, however. Through our own laziness we buy processed food from supermarkets. Therefore the building blocks of our cells have simply not been given the nutrients they need. The over-weight children of the recent generation are succumbing to heart disease, diabetes and arthritis much sooner than earlier generations who were brought up on whole, healthy foods.

Osteoporosis, the honeycombing of the bones which leads to fractures, is also caused because we have not been feeding our bones the minerals and living enzymes they need.

Secondly, the Genesis diet rids the body of food allergies, and eliminates rheumatoid flare-ups. An acid diet will produce great pain in the body, as gout sufferers know. Uric acid builds up and can cause excruciating pain.

The Genesis diet consists of alkaline foods, which in time will completely remove the pain caused by acids. This does not happen overnight! If years of acid foods have built up acidity levels in the body, it will take several weeks of correct nutrition and enemas to detoxify the body, and become pain free. However, once free from the addiction to damaging food, an arthritis sufferer will never want to return to the crippling pain. The desire for the wrong foods simply disappears, as the body responds to the living enzymes it needs.

The word "arthritis" comes from the Latin root "arthro" meaning joint. Any disease that ends in an 'itis' means an inflammation, so arthritis means inflammation of a joint. Basically, a joint is the place where two bones meet, and the bone ends are covered in cartilage which is a smooth and softer, a less brittle surface than bone. The cartilage effectively protects the bone end.

So that the joints can move freely, there is a fluid between them which is held in the joint space by a membrane or skin. The fluid is called synovial fluid and the membrane is called the synovial membrane.

The joint works through a mechanical process whereby a muscle stretching from one side of it to the other contracts to make the joint move in one direction, and relaxes to make it move in the other direction. The part of the muscle that is attached to the bone is called the tendon.

For a joint to work in one direction there must be something holding it in place in the other direction and this is called the ligament. Little cushions called bursa, plural bursae, keep the muscle and joint from rubbing together. Inflammation of a bursa it is called bursitis, inflammation of the tendon is tendonitis, and inflammation of the joint is arthritis.

Normally a healthy joint consists of strong bones which in themselves are a matrix of protein, principally collagen, calcium, magnesium and phosphorus, which make the bone very strong. Cartilage protects the two bones from rubbing together and this cartilage is made partly from collagen and also from an interesting group of substances called muco-poly-saccharides which are protein-carbohydrate complexes.

Bones and cartilage, like every other part of the body, are actually made from the food we eat, so we need to eat raw living enzymes to build healthy bones, cartilage, and supporting tendons and muscles. We also need to eat an alkaline diet, because an acid diet causes arthritic pain and gradually destroys bones.

If our posture is in a poor state of alignment, or if we habitually stress or strain a particular joint, this repetitive damage will eventually lead to a gradual breaking down of the cartilage. If the cartilage deteriorates enough, the bone ends become uneven, causing restricted movement and pain.

In arthritis we find the formation of little bone spurs which are called osteocytes. In advanced arthritis when the body is continually in an inflammatory state, we lose the ability to keep calcium where it should be, and this calcium can be dumped in soft tissues causing pain. In rheumatoid arthritis the bone ends can actually become fused together. Our aim is to enable the body to rebuild its collagen matrix and restore healthy bones, cartilage and synovial membranes on the Genesis diet and lifestyle.

There are different types of arthritis. Osteoarthritis is classified as a degenerative disease - one that occurs in many people and seems to be a consequence of gradual degeneration, through sports injuries, accidents, or other forms of repetitive strain and damage.

It is important to understand that arthritis can also be caused by impaired body chemistry. Our bodies have a system of glands called the endocrine glands. These glands produce hormones which are designed to control our blood sugar level, our sex hormone balance, reactions to stress, rate of metabolism and they also control how we use calcium in the body. When people have lost this ability to balance their calcium correctly, they develop arthritis.

It is therefore possible that endocrine abuse through stress, over many years, can lead to losing this vital balance. As well as psychological stress giving rise to bad body chemistry, physical stress is imposed on the body through wear and tear, and also through the intake of meat, wheat, wine and dairy, cooked foods and carbonated drinks, and stimulants as alcohol, tea, coffee and sugar, which are all acid forming in the body.

The body must be detoxified in order to address the problem of arthritis, rather than masking the pain by taking chemical pain killers or non-steroidal anti-inflammatory drugs, NSAIDS, or steroids like prednisolone, which cause great damage to the digestive and endocrine systems if taken for a prolonged period.

The diet should be alkaline forming rather than acid forming, and in order to start this de-toxification one must flush out the system rather like clearing rust out of a machine. The best de-toxifying element is water, inside and outside the body.

Warm water cleanses more efficiently than cold water, so warm water and ginger should be drunk several times a day. Fresh ginger root has been used for thousands of years as a natural anti-inflammatory without side effects, and it has a strongly detoxifying and settling effect on the body.

The infusion is made by boiling pure water in a saucepan with some chopped fresh root ginger. I make a sufficient quantity for each day early in the morning, and then keep the liquid ready to heat each time I need it during the day. I strain the liquid into a mug and add a fresh slice of lemon, which is an alkaliser, and a half teaspoon of pure honey each time. I drink a mug on waking, and on the hour throughout the day. It is also an excellent cleanser taken before sleeping, so that the body de-toxifies during its rest period.

If I am working away from home I take my ginger, honey and lemon drink in a thermos to keep hot so that I am not tempted to drink tea or coffee. However, restaurants will always be able to produce hot water with a slice of lemon, even if they do not have ginger.

In addition to this ginger drink, it is vital to maintain the carrot, apple, pineapple and green juice of the Genesis diet, which provide the building blocks for the cells so they can repair themselves. Interestingly, the body cannot absorb inorganic minerals, only organic ones, so the mineral supplements we buy in bottles are not assimilated properly into the body. We need "The Real Thing!" The only way we can absorb the minerals we need so much is the way God intended, organically, through the phytosynthesis in plants of the Genesis Diet.

We have to be faithful to this healing, God-given diet if we want to be free from pain. Once the body has become acidified through a bad diet, it will react very badly when acids are re-introduced. One glass of champagne for a celebration will result in a week of arthritic pain. If you cheat, you only cheat yourself!

If one has been on pain killing drugs for some time, stomach ulcers usually develop, adding to the misery of pain. Interestingly, even three days on the Genesis juices will usually eliminate ulcer pain that has been caused by the non steroidal anti-inflammatory drugs called NSAID's.

This diet is also much more effective than the acidifying milk diet prescribed by most doctors. Tagamet and Zantac, which is often prescribed for patients with ulcers are now thought to contribute towards Alzheimer's Disease.

So often one chemical drug causes side effects necessitating taking another drug to alleviate the second problem! A vicious circle! This makes more profit for the pharmaceutical companies! Some pharmacists have become so disillusioned that they have even stopped practising medical pharmacy and gone into natural health care instead. One ex-pharmacist told me that there is a cost to be paid for every drug one takes, and it is not just paid in money.

The Genesis lifestyle cleanses the liver and helps keep weight down, which is good for the body generally. This in itself relieves pressure on the hip and knee joints. If something more substantial is needed while de-toxifying, organic vegetable home-made soup may be drunk. Make it using virgin olive oil in a deep saucepan, adding a chopped onion and optional garlic. When gently softened, add the chopped organic vegetables; carrots, cabbage, broccoli, and celery are the most nutritious.

Only add tomatoes or potatoes if there is no allergy to the deadly nightshade family of vegetables, to which they belong. The only way to find out for sure is try to introduce them gently. If the pain returns, eliminate them! Do remember to make soup with distilled water only, as vegetables absorb all the toxins from tap water.

Once the vegetables are softened, remove from the heat and blend with a stainless steel electric blending wand, right in the hot soup in the saucepan. Decorate with chopped parsley, chives or coriander, the raw "green plant" of the Genesis Diet.

The second type of arthritis, rheumatoid arthritis, however, is very much connected with the immune system. Rheumatoid arthritis is an auto-immune disease, where the immune system is reacting to the body itself instead of just reacting to invaders. Rheumatoid factor can be detected by a blood test which proves the presence of this immunological inflammatory factor.

In osteo-arthritis there is a gradual worsening of pain and stiffness in a weight bearing joint, whereas in rheumatoid arthritis is typified by a sudden flare-up and sudden remission. In rheumatoid arthritis the joints affected may not be weight bearing joints, but may be the elbows or wrists. Rheumatoid arthritis also tends to occur on both sides of the body - bilaterally rather than unilaterally - as in osteoarthritis.

Despite these differences between osteoarthritis and rheumatoid arthritis, there are also some common contributory factors and ways in which we can deal with these problems, and also the problem of osteoporosis.

One of these is hormonal imbalance. The thyroid endocrine gland producing calcitonin and the parathyroid glands producing parathormone, control the calcium balance in the body. If these glands do not work properly a loss of calcium from the bone is likely.

Another hormonal factor, particularly in women, is the balance between oestrogen and progesterone. The background here is that there are two types of cells in the bones; osteoblasts which are responsible for building new bone and osteoplasts which are responsible for getting rid of old bone.

For the past twenty years, doctors have recommended women to take oestrogen in hormone replacement therapy believing that this will prevent the loss of old bone. This however has led to proliferation of oestrogen-fired breast and ovarian cancer in women. The Genesis diet, eliminating animal protein, contains no harmful oestrogen, but provides the exact balance God ordained that we should have.

It is now understood that the osteoblast is a more important factor because this stimulates the formation of new bone, which should be a continuous process. This process is dependent on progesterone. Studies have shown that women who have sufficient progesterone actually have four times the increase in bone mass density compared with those who use synthetic oestrogen in HRT.

A gradual excess of oestrogen or deficiency of progesterone can result in osteoporosis and this is also a precursor for arthritic type conditions.

The general endocrine system is very much affected by stress and by the use of stimulants. It is advisable therefore to test for an underlying glucose intolerance factor.

Allergies are always present in the case of rheumatoid arthritis and sometimes in the case of osteoarthritis. The two main orthodox medical treatments of both are hormone based or steroid-based medication such as cortisol or cortisone drugs, or non-steroidal ant-inflammatory drugs (NSAID's).

Doctors in general practice only receive a few hours training in nutrition. They prescribe for their patients what they have been taught to prescribe in medical schools, which are often subsidized and funded by the drug companies. Even if these doctors know the Genesis nutritional regime, they often say that their patients would never stick to such a stringent diet. They invariably opt for the drugs - a prescription of NSAID's or steroids for short-term relief. Neither addresses the actual cause of the arthritis, or cures it long term.

Unfortunately these drugs are known to have two side effects. They increase the permeability of the gut, and so make the body more allergic, and in the long run they seem to speed up the progression of arthritis.

The gut permeability factor is very interesting and important. We do not know whether rheumatoid arthritis is caused by an allergy, or whether an allergy develops due to using these drugs; but rheumatoid arthritis sufferers are always highly allergic to certain foods.

Allergy is a very tricky area to research, but findings suggest that foods people react to most commonly are wheat, dairy, animal protein, oranges, grains, eggs, wine and caffeine – coffee, tea and chocolate. None of these are consumed on the Genesis diet.

So the body needs to detox. The best way is to start the arthritis cure by spending a day drinking only hot water, flavoured with anti-inflammatory ginger, a touch of honey and a twist of lemon which alkalises the body. Of course this is perfect for weight loss, which in turn will relieve the stress on the joints.

This is a food fast. Fasting is biblical for those who want to purify themselves and concentrate completely on God. We read in 2 Chronicles 20:3 that King Jehoshaphat led the people of Judah to fast and afterwards overcame a vast attacking army.

In the book of Esther 4:15 we see how Esther led a three day fast in Susa. After that she found favour with the King and the Jewish people were saved. In the first chapter of the book of Daniel, verse 8-20, Daniel, Hannaniah, Mishael and Azariah fasted on water and vegetables for ten days. They became healthier and stronger than the other young men who ate King Nebuchadnezzar's fine wine and rich food.

It has been proven that as long as we drink enough water and the living enzymes of fresh juices, we can cut down on our solid food intake for a few days with great benefits to our health.

After three days on the liquid only diet, which gives the body a chance to detoxify, we should introduce fresh, high water content salad for lunch with fresh lettuce, pineapple, cucumber, sweet corn, plum tomatoes, seeds and nuts. Add a honey, mustard lemon and virgin olive oil based dressing. Warldof salad is also good, combining crisp chopped celery with sliced apples and walnuts. As on the Genesis diet, supper is home made raw avocado soup, or occasionally a lightly cooked soup, a large fresh salad with a few lightly steamed vegetables.

Arthritics will stay pain free and will not want to return to the foods that harmed them. Once the body has been restored to health, one loses the cravings for damaging foods.

Romans 12:2 says
"Be not conformed to this world, but be transformed by the renewing of your minds, so that you may discern what is the will of God"

When entertaining we can introduce people to the delights of the Genesis diet. When being invited out, simply tell friends that you are the easiest and least expensive guest they will ever have! You only want to eat vegetables instead of meat or fish!

Most people are in need of healing from a degenerative disease, and you will always find at least one of your companions at dinner listening eagerly.

In hotels and restaurants one can simply tell the staff that you are on a special diet. Order bottled still water, and choose something benign, like soup, cruditées, avocado pear, a dish of vegetables or wholegrain rice, followed by fresh fruit salad, and finish the meal with hot water, lemon and honey instead of coffee.

If one sticks to 80% juices and raw salads, and is completely clear of arthritis, one can try 20% cooked food, and may eventually introduce a little oily fish, like salmon, provided it has been caught fresh in pure waters.

Chicken and red meats are, however, nowadays so filled with antibiotics, steroids and hormones that they make unhealthy eating. Avian flu and mad cow disease confirm God's Word in Genesis 1:29 and 30. We are not supposed to be eating animal protein - chicken, eggs or meat. They are acid forming and will fire arthritis again. Nuts and beans with rice provide protein without the damaging additives.

Alcohol is a depressant and destroys vitamins. It damages the liver, the pancreas and the kidneys. It also impairs brain function and co-ordination, and an excess reduces us to a coma and eventually death! The grape is acid, so wine and brandy are more harmful to arthritics than grain based whisky, or potato based gin. Tannin, rennin and meta-bi-suphites which are used in wine production, are particularly noxious.

Most people are happy to simply order bottled water, as athletes do, but if you feel you want to blend with the rest of the party, clear apple juice looks exactly like white wine when served in a wine glass, just as grape or cranberry juice look exactly like red wine. Both fruit juices are cleansing and boost the immune system, while alcohol damages it. As the party progresses and you see people lose co-ordination and slur their words while you remain in control, you will be glad that you are on the healthy Genesis diet! You will rejoice even more the next morning!

Once there is inflammation in the body, the body starts to produce free radicals. The invader also produces free radicals. These are very damaging and leave the body open to disease. There is a theory that rheumatoid arthritis is caused by viral or bacterial infection. Therefore anti-oxidant vitamins A, C and E, together with selenium and zinc could be supplemented in addition to starting the Genesis Diet. In rheumatoid arthritis these free radicals attack the synovial membranes and therefore anti-oxidants alleviate this inflammation.

Vitamin C is doubly important - firstly as an anti-oxidant and secondly because it is required in conjunction with calcium, magnesium, phosphorus, Vitamin D, and boron to provide the essential collagen which forms the matrix of bones and cartilage.

One of the most exciting areas in relation to the treatment of arthritis lies in natural anti-inflammatory agents such a ginger and essential fatty acids. The reason why non-steroidal anti-inflammatory drugs, such as ibuprofen, work is that they affect the levels in the body of certain hormone-like substances in the body called prostaglandins. These prostaglandins are very much involved in inflammatory responses. They are made from essential fatty acids which we take in our diet in the form of nuts and olive oil.

There are two families of essential fatty acids, linoleic and linolenic. Linoleic acid is known as "omega 6" which comes principally from seeds and oils such as sunflower and sesame seeds, as God directs in the Genesis diet.

Provided you have enough vitamin B6, zinc, magnesium and biotin, you can turn the linoleic acid into gamma linolenic acid which is found in evening primrose oil and borage oil. This gamma linolenic acid will in due course turn into prostaglandins that have a very strong anti-inflammatory effect. Many studies have now been performed using evening primrose oil or borage oil to measure this effect.

The other essential fatty acid is called linolenic acid which comes from nuts, seeds and oils; the richest source being pumpkin seed, flaxseed oil and linseed. Linolenic acid is transformed into eicosapentanoic acid or EPA, and dehydroepiandrosterone or DHEA. It has been proved that EPA and DHEA derived from linoleic acid go on to produce anti-inflammatory prostoglandins.

Dietary sources of gamma linolenic acid as in evening primrose oil and dietary sources of EPA fish oil have also been shown to reduce inflammation. An evening primrose oil capsule of 500 mg's, only contains 10% of GLA, so one only actually derives 50 mg's from the capsule.

116

As you need 300 mg a day to get a positive anti-inflammatory effect, you need to take six capsules a day, which is expensive. However, one can take a high strength borage oil or starflower oil capsules which provides 300mg's just in one capsule.

Linolenic acid should also be supplied by sprinkling sesame seeds on salads and making one's own nutritious bars with linseeds, sesame seeds, honey, raisins and crushed almonds. Mix the ingredients together, press into an oiled baking tin. Leave to set in the fridge and then cut into fingers.

Calcium balance depends on vitamin D status, stress levels and weight bearing exercise. It is also necessary to minimise protein because protein makes the blood more acid, causing the body to leach calcium from the bone.

The Genesis diet is therefore a huge boost to our calcium requirement. It does not contain damaging animal protein, and it is rich in slow releasing complex carbohydrates, with a plentiful supply of essential fatty acids, found in the seeds.

Importantly, the Genesis diet is low in saturated fat, which blocks the body's ability to use EFA's. Some foods are rather deceptive in that they re labelled "low in polyunsaturated fats". However margarine contains damaged polyunsaturated fats - which are hydrogenated, or transfatty acids. They will actually block the EFA's.

If you are trying to cure existing severe arthritis, it is wise to supplement a few vitamins. Pantothenic acid (Vitamin B5) helps produce adrenal hormones. Many tests have now shown significantly reduced pain, stiffness and inflammation when 500-1000 mg's of pantothenic acid is used. This is far above the recommended daily allowance, or recommended daily allowance, but completely non-toxic and well worth a try.

Vitamin B3 in the form of niacinamide does not have the violent flushing reaction of simple B3. This has been researched over many years by a pioneer called Dr. William Kaufmann. He has tried to call his work on niacinamide to the attention of rheumatologists, nutritionists and gerontologists. This has been overshadowed by the advent of quick-acting but damaging cortisone. Doctors have also been sceptical because of his use of a huge 1000 mg dose.

However, Canadian research showed that ulnar deviation and Heberden's nodes on the fingers could be reversed in a three month period by supplementing 1000 mg's of niacinamide a day in two divided doses. The patients have continued forty years on this dose and their arthritis has not returned. If ordinary niacin is used, an unpleasant blushing or hot flush is felt in the body, so it is better to stick to the niacinamide variety which had exactly the same beneficial effect on arthritis.

The best vitamin B complex I have found is a powder in capsule form which does not smell unpleasant. It is made by Biocare Ltd., www.biocare.co.uk Lakeside, 180 Lifford Lane, Kings Norton, Birmingham B30 3NU. Tel 44(0)121 433 3727. Vitamin B is needed by the central nervous system, and has a calming effect which is important in arthritis, as well as the particular properties listed above. Vitamin B6 works well in carpal tunnel syndrome. A B-complex vitamin is helpful for those on a vegan diet as it provides B12.

Regarding minerals, selenium is very important, but zinc, copper, iron and manganese are also necessary to promote an enzyme called SOD or sodium oxidising dismutase. Too much copper or iron can make arthritis worse, so the right balance must be found for each person. Wearing of copper bracelets has varying results, but is worth a try.

These four minerals attack the damaging free radicals, but do not completely remove them. They then need to be disarmed by glutathione peroxidase which is dependent on selenium. This careful balance must be maintained, otherwise iron and copper can actually make arthritis worse. For this reason a complete mineral screen like a hair mineral analysis test should be given by a natural health professional.

Polymyalgia, known as fibromyalgia in the USA, relates to pain in the muscles rather than the joints. This may be caused by muscle tension because of an imbalance between calcium and magnesium. Magnesium, found in green vegetables, relaxes muscles. There is also a possibility that the muscle cells cannot turn glucose into energy through a blockage due to lack of magnesium malate. Mallic acid is found in apple juice and magnesium in green vegetables.

Boron in vegetables also improves arthritis by assisting in the assimilation of calcium. Once the Genesis lifestyle is established, and the arthritis gone, extra supplementation will not be needed. The living enzymes and the essential oils from the nuts and seeds will suffice, as God intended.

Exercise and posture plays a part in assimilating nutrients because the spine lengthens when we are lying down, and the compression of vertebrae is released. Nutrients in the surrounding tissue are then able to be sucked into the bone, cartilage and joint cells. Exercising to increase the joint space by loosening and releasing them this will be very helpful. Lying on the ground with the spine flat on the floor and gradually edging the discs apart by wriggling the base of the spine further from the shoulders on each out breath, and then resting in this position for some time, is particularly helpful. When pain is localized, it is helpful to put two soft tennis balls under the back in the painful area, and move to massage the area until the pain is eased.

Having the right posture is vitally important. Standing against a wall, and aligning the spine so that the back of the head, shoulders, pelvis, knees and heels touch the wall is a good way of checking ones own alignment. Sitting at a computer, or cricking the neck to hold a telephone receiver, impose stress on the neck and back. Soft tissue massage should be used regularly to relax the muscles. The spine is critical because it houses the main central nervous system and the alignment of the glands.

Water also plays an essential part in arthritis because most of us do not drink the required two litres of pure water a day. Aim for a glass of water every waking hour.

We should also use hydro therapy in the form of hot or cold compresses, and alkalising baths of Epsom salts, which reduce the acidity of the body. This is especially useful after a massage or exercise session, as acid crystals will have been released which are then removed in the bath.

Herbs like yucca, aloe vera, devils claw, cats claw and quercetin, a bioflavinoid, may also be helpful for those suffering from arthritis. The Genesis diet eliminates damaging stimulants like sugars, margarine, alcohol and fried foods. It also ensures the absorption of adequate living enzymes and vitamins in fruit and vegetables. Minerals are derived from cruciferous - crunchy, structured - vegetables, and essential fatty acids are supplied from nuts and seeds.

This diet also avoids saturated fat and excess protein which are found in dairy produce and meat. Dairy produce, incidentally, produces mucous which as well as firing arthritis, will also exacerbate catarrh and chest infections.

Linus Pauling, who won the Nobel Peace Prize for his work on Vitamin C, recommended taking very much more than had been used in trials. Small amounts do not work, and we need to take as much as each individual needs, to bowel tolerance. When the body is saturated, the rest will be excreted. Vitamin C is probably the most important supplement needed for boosting the immune system.

We also need vitamin E, another anti-oxidant, to oxygenate the blood and give energy. We should have at least 800 international units a day of the natural variety, d alpha tocopherol, and those who need an auto-immune boost can take up to 1000 i.u.

Vitamin A, also anti-oxidant, protects membranes and should be taken up to a 75,000 strength. This can be taken in a joint oil capsules with Vitamin D which protects the bones. Sunbathing also provides Vitamin D for bones.

Vitamin B has already been suggested in the BioCare form, which does not contain yeast. Add 1000mg of vitamin B3 and 1000mg of

B5 to alleviate arthritis, and a 1000 mg of GLA or flax-seed oil and 1200-1800 mg of EPA, or pure fish oil.

Ginkgo biloba restores circulation in stiff and calcified joints, and the enzyme COQ10 taken in 90 mg doses is an important anti-oxidant and also a memory restorer.

An amino acid called DLPA seems to be a harmless painkiller which can be used if it is very difficult to come off the NSAID's initially, and while one is waiting for the new nutrition to have the desired effect in reducing the pain and inflammation of arthritis.

Leaky gut syndrome is caused by stress, causing hydrochloric acid to flood into the stomach. This eventually destroys the villi in the intestine. Refined wheat and possibly all wheat, can no longer be absorbed and this is why some people develop arthritis after on-going stress. Lacto-bacillus capsules should be taken with every meal to restore the intestinal balance, and are essential whenever antibiotics are taken. They are very helpful in irritable bowel disease, which is caused by leaky gut and gluten allergy.

It is therefore essential to learn to manage stress better. We either make good body chemistry or bad body chemistry according to the thoughts we think. Stress flushes acids like cortisol and adrenaline into the body, and this eventually leads to adrenal burn out.

This then causes calcium to be leached from bone to protect the vital heart muscle, and this calcium does not return to the bone but may lodge in muscles and ligaments instead, increasing pain. For this reason, gentle exercise is beneficial, so that the natural flight or fight stress reaction can be released, and the body chemistry returns to normal. In modern society it is less easy to fight or flee, so we tend to live with our stress by hunching our shoulders, gritting our teeth and generally tensing up.

Most arthritis is cold reactive, so it is important to be warm enough. A warm, dry climate helps tremendously, and one must keep out of humid, cold, rainy and windy weather as much as possible. Gentle exercise such a walk in the morning sun, is helpful. This is particularly calming to the body, mind and spirit, especially when taken in fresh air by natural sources of energy, trees, mountains, lakes or the sea.

Swimming in hot water is helpful, as are long, hot baths using a solution of bicarbonate of soda, or Epsom salts. Salts are also highly recommended to take internally. Taking the waters has been a cure for thousands of years, and thalassotherapy using mud or seaweed packs relieves arthritis in a dramatic way.

An inexpensive form of these body wraps can be achieved by soaking crepe bandages in the salts dissolved in hot water, and wrapping them around arthritic joints. Cover the wet bandages with polythene, apply hot water bottles to keep the pack warm for half an hour, and cover with blankets and rest. A hot bath afterwards, followed by a hot oil massage or arthritis cream, will work wonders.

Lymph drainage shifts the acid crystals released from the joints, and also stimulates the lymph and blood circulation. Lymph drainage by a trained aromatherapist will help tremendously. It is important to establish a regular practice so that one can relax completely in capable hands to gain maximum benefit.

Colonic irrigation performed by a specialist or a home enema is a quick way to eliminate toxicity. This should be followed by a day of drinking pure water and carrot and apple juice for maximum benefit. Trans-Act plasters containing ibuprofen can be applied locally to very painful joints, and are particularly good for back pain. They can be peeled off the skin and stuck to smooth plastic surface and re applied after the bath or shower, as their efficacy lasts more than 24 hours.

In conclusion, arthritis can be understood as a degenerative disease which can be controlled by a sensible regime of de-toxification on the Genesis diet, light exercise, hydrotherapy, relaxation techniques and boost to the immune system with supplements.

Osteoporosis can be avoided by giving the body the building and repairing cells from the living enzymes it needs.

Like the dry bones in Ezekiel, returning to God's Word will revive our bones and let us live again!

Chapter Ten

The Greatest Healing

Jesus says: "Today you will be with me in Paradise" Luke 23:43

The greatest healing, greater than any physical healing, is our salvation. Our earthly tents inevitably wear out, and are thankfully left behind. But our spirit lives on, and the destination of our souls is our choice.

For Christians, dying is our everlasting healing and home coming to God, a return to our eternal home. It is the essence of joy and peace. It means we are safe for ever, and that we will never lose the people we love, who also believe in Jesus.

We do not lose them when they die. They are in our present because we are all one in the Body of Christ, just as the stars are still there on a cloudy night, although we cannot see them temporarily. And they will also be in our future when we are all together with the Lord. Having lost a beloved daughter, parents and husband, I am living witness to the truth that the only healing for bereavement is Jesus.

My good shepherd, Bernard, my beloved husband, died of cancer while I was writing this book. He had not been on the Genesis diet; like so many he felt he was so healthy he did not need it! He had been carrying his golf bag on the golf course all summer, and he had been driving up and down through France, Spain and Portugal between our homes. But once the cancer caught hold, he died within eight weeks of diagnosis, in great physical discomfort. He was truly courageous. We tried the laetrile but it was too late. The lymphoma had spread all over his body.

Bernard's very painful death motivated me even more to finish this book quickly. It is so important to be on the Genesis diet, to build up the immune system and prevent disease. We cannot just fill the body with laetrile when we are critically ill, expecting years of toxins to be eliminated and the body healed. We have to be on the living diet.

I think one of the reasons I was healed three years ago was that I had already been a vegetarian for 20 years and had never liked alcohol. Although I had not yet discovered the truth about the raw living enzymes on Genesis 1:29 and 30, I had relatively few toxins in my body.

Although Bernard was not healed physically, he did, in fact, have the greatest healing. He had always been a Christian, and used to read his well worn RAF pocket Bible. He had loved services in the thirteenth century chapel at St. Edmund Hall, his old college at Oxford, and he was treasurer of our church in Jersey which we attended every Sunday. Only three weeks before he died, he bravely attended an all island evening Healing Service in the church. I had flown a South African surgeon and a Baptist Minister into the island and we all spoke on healing in the Bible.

The music was wonderful. It was music from the Benny Hinn Healing Crusades, many were healed spiritually and are now healing physically on the Genesis Diet.

Bernard was greatly touched by the service. Although he was not healed physically, he received the greatest healing of all. He came to a real understanding of Jesus as his saviour. We had family Communions around his bed, and he was visited nearly every day by our dear friend Graham, who leads Alpha courses with me and hosts a wonderful home group. The three of us had much prayer together. Bernard said he had never known such love. Of all his friends, RAF, sailing and City friends, he said the love of Jesus was incomparable.

We held a wonderful thanksgiving service for his life, with the RAF flag on his coffin. I had the immense privilege of wearing his wartime medals on my robes and leading the service. We had 300 lovely letters about Bernard and the money which was raised in his memory now provides beds and a heater for AIDS orphans in

Lesotho, a mission started by a friend of ours, Jill Kinsey, a courageous RAF widow who loves Jesus and walks the walk.

For those who have given their lives to Jesus, and lived for Him, going home is a great celebration, at the end of a fruitful mission, when Jesus says in Matthew 25:21 we will hear the words *"Well done, you good and faithful servant."* As my daughter felt, "the term is over, the holidays begin!"

The Bible has much to say about heaven. My father used to quote what Jesus himself said in John 14:2,
"In my Father's house are many rooms, if it were not so I would have told you. I am going there to prepare a place for you, and if I go and prepare a place for you, I will come back and take you to be with me."

If we try to guess how wonderful heaven will be, our imagination falls short, because
Isaiah 64:41 and 1 Corinthians 2:9 both tell us:
"No eye has seen, no ear has heard, no mind has conceived, what God has prepared for those who love him"

Certainly there is no grief there. Revelation 21:4 tells us:
"God will wipe every tear from their eyes. There will be no more death or mourning or crying or pain, for the old order of things has passed away."

Not everyone will reach heaven, however. As with everything in life, it is a matter of free will. The Bible says that if we deny Jesus on earth, he will not acknowledge us when we stand in judgement before his Father, God. Although there is mercy, and no one knows if another receives Christ in their last moments, there is no certainty unless we acknowledge Jesus during our lifetime.

Our span of life on earth comes to an end eventually for us all, as Psalm 103 says:
"As for man, his days are like grass,
He flourishes like a flower of the field;
The wind blows over it and it is gone,
And it's place remembers it no more."

When facing death, the unbeliever is completely and hopelessly out of his depth.

But for the faithful, God says in Isaiah 43:

"Fear not, for I have redeemed you;
I have summoned you by name; you are mine.
When you pass through the waters
I will be with you,
And when you pass through the rivers
They will not sweep over you.
When you walk through the fire,
You will not be burned,
The flames will not set you ablaze.
For I am the Lord, you God,
The Holy One of Israel, your Saviour.

When I was given only a few weeks to live, facing a painful and cruel death, these words were my greatest comfort. Never had I been so glad to be a Christian – I was assured that Jesus, who had suffered far worse pain than I would, would be with me as I passed through the rivers, and my Advocate on Judgement Day. I was also assured that if God granted me a gracious life extension, and I was healed, He would be with me and empower me to witness about Him.

My daughter had been sure of her faith and said she had had an angel on her bed the day she was diagnosed. Although she had drifted in and out of consciousness for several hours before she died, at the very last moment she sat up and looked up expectantly as though her angel had come for her. When my mother, father and husband died, the same thing happened. They were sure of their faith and their salvation. They were led home.

Jesus promised one of the thieves who was being crucified next to him, that he would be with Him that day in paradise. Why was this convicted criminal going to heaven with Jesus while the other thief was not? Because he came to believe, even in his dying moments, that Jesus was the son of God. The other thief did not come to believe, and died without hope of salvation, like so many in our world.

How could Jesus promise salvation? Because He is the Son of God. He came willingly into the world to save sinners. Have you ever despaired of others' efforts, and thought that the only way to do something properly was to do it yourself? That is exactly what God did. He came to earth as a man, and suffered all the indignities, difficulties and trials of life.

He did only good. He healed all who asked. He taught as no one has ever taught before or since.. He performed miracle after miracle. He brought the New Covenant to us. And when His message of love was rejected by the religious hierarchy, he willingly went to the cross for us. He had to die that appalling death to atone for the sins of the whole world, which he did because He loves us. The price had to be paid, and He is our ransom.

Why did He have to die? God is a just and holy God, as well as a merciful one. Therefore sin has to be punished. This is bad news for us, as we have all sinned. As Romans 3:23 says
"All have sinned and fall short of the glory of God, and are justified freely by his grace through redemption that came by Christ Jesus."

We are only saved because Jesus took the punishment for us. Where does this leave us? Is everyone going to heaven? Can their good deeds get them there?
There are many good humanists in the world, what happens to them?

The Bible does not promise salvation to all, only believers in Jesus Christ.
"For God so loved the world that he gave his one and only son, that whoever believes in him shall not perish but have eternal life." John 3:16

So we have a choice to make while we are still alive. It is the most important choice we will ever make. However long we live on this earth, we cannot get to heaven in our bodies. Like seed being sown, we have to die to this life, and our remains buried, in order to gain heaven.

127

Jesus said: " I tell you the truth, unless a grain of wheat falls into the earth and dies, it remains only a single seed. But if it dies, it produces many seeds. The man who loves his life will lose it, while the man who hates his life in this world will keep it for eternal life. Whoever serves me must follow me, and where I am, my servant also will be. My Father will honour the one who serves me." John 12:24

How ever wealthy, how ever protected we are in our lifetimes, we enter and depart earthly life alone, helpless and vulnerable, like the poorest people on earth. Jesus says if we do not acknowledge him and do his work on earth, He will not stand as our advocate when we come to Judgement Day before God.

In Mark 8:36, Jesus says: *"For what good is it for a man to gain the whole world, yet forfeit his soul? Or what can a man give in exchange for his soul? If anyone is ashamed of me and my words in this adulterous and sinful generation, the Son of Man will be ashamed of him when he comes into His Father's glory with the holy angels.*

As well as believing in Jesus, we have to have done his work in the world while we were here. Matthew 25:41-46 puts it very clearly – *"Depart from me, you who are cursed, into the fire prepared for the devil and his angels. For I was hungry and you gave me nothing to eat, I was thirsty and you gave me nothing to drink, I was a stranger and you did not invite me in, I needed clothes and you did not clothe me, I was sick and in prison and you did not look after me. Whenever you did not do for one of the least of these, you did not do unto me." Then they will go away to eternal punishment, but the righteous to eternal life."*

As always, God gives us free choice. Where we spend eternity depends on what we choose.

Some people may put off the decision while they continue to enjoy their selfish lives. But we never know when our lives with end, as Jesus said in Luke 12:20 to the complacent man who was satisfied with his hoarded riches *"This very night your life will be demanded from you."* We must always be prepared for judgement.

James 4:14 says *"What is your life? You are a mist that appears for a little while and then vanishes."* We are only here a short time!

That short time is put into proper perspective if we look at it like a tapestry. If we look at the wrong side of the tapestry, we just see an untidy jumble of loose ends. But when we turn the tapestry over, all is revealed. We suddenly see the whole picture. The design was there all the time, although when looking at the wrong side we just could not see it. But God, the designer, had a plan all along.

The more we pray and read our Bibles, the more the Holy Spirit helps us to understand the things that happen in our lives. I do not believe in coincidences, only God-incidences. I believe that it is a God incidence that you are reading this very page!

And of course there is an infinitely bigger picture – the work we have wrought in the lives of others. Then we realise how important it is to only sow good things into others' lives, only to speak words of healing, of encouragement to them. We can heal others by our words, and our love.

We begin to understand that every little stitch is necessary to the whole work. Every person we have met, every seed we have sown, has contributed to the final work. The people who annoy us and hurt us make us grow just as much as the ones who inspire us. When you make a friend out of an old enemy, through the love, reconciliation and forgiveness of Jesus, it is an unspeakable joy. Indeed we must forgive, so that God can forgive us! This is what the whole world needs, reconciliation through the Lord, and never more needed between different religious factions.

I believe it is really important to look for the blessings God gives us every day. When we start noting them and writing them down, it makes impressive reading. What a way to go to bed at night, counting your blessings, and planning how you can bless someone else the next day – "Lord, what do you want me to do for you tomorrow?"

To learn about blessings, you have to read God's Word. Blessings have not been taught in the church since the time of Constantine in 325 AD. Constantine did not become a Christian until two weeks before his death, and during his life he tried to make the priesthood as unpopular as he could. He forbad priests to speak of blessings or prosperity from God, on pain of death. He demanded that every preacher take the oath of poverty.

In those days very few people could read, and so it was in the power of the priests to withhold precious biblical information from the people. They ruled by fear. As the Roman Empire crumbled, the Emperors saw another way of controlling the masses through religiosity. This religiosity has done enormous harm in keeping people ignorant of the accessibility, love and blessings of God as found in the Bible.

The Bible does not mention praying to Mary, Jesus' mother. It forbids worship of idols and icons. The Bible actually condemns ritualistic and ostentatious prayers repeated by cant with the mouth but not from the depths of the heart. Many churches are therefore unbiblical.

Blessings were not preached. It is only in the last few hundred years that people can read their own Bibles and find the truths for themselves. Jesus said that he had come to fulfil the Scriptures, by which he meant the Old Testament, which contains 332 prophecies about His life and death. Such evidence in incontrovertible.

It is essential to have some quiet time with the Lord each day, to get to know Him by reading the whole Bible through several times a year. The whole Bible can be read in fifty six hours; if we only read three chapters a day and five on Sunday, we could complete it within twelve months. Once the Holy Spirit leads us, we find it the most fascinating book in the world! All life is there, and as well as meeting God, we meet ourselves and people we know again and again.

Those who find difficulty are usually reading a Bible whose language is outdated. There is nothing sacrosanct about the King

James Bible, it is merely an English translation of the original Hebrew of the Old Testament and Greek of the New.

We need an understandable translation, such as the New Life Bibles published by Bible Society, www.biblesociety.org.uk, and the New International Version, which contains good explanatory notes. The Life Application Bible explains the Hebrew or Greek origin of the words and includes profiles of biblical characters, maps, charts and a wonderful index which is like a mini concordance. It is a perfect study Bible.

When we spend time in God's Word, real healing takes place. When I was very ill in hospital, a friend sent me a CD of the world famous Greek evangelist Benny Hinn reading a selection of biblical healing texts from Genesis to Revelation. Listening to these, and also the Bible Society CD's of the New Testament, helped me to heal. I played them all the time I was alone, and they were a wonderful refuge at night, when the pain was bad. I played them on a Walkman with earphones, so that whether sleeping or waking, I was saturated with the Word of God.

Paul tells us in Galatians that we reap as we sow. We also learn to plant seed, as God commands. We cannot expect healings and blessings if we are robbing God.
The Old Testament teaches us about the giving God expects of us. There are festivals and times of the year when we must give in order to stay in the blessing.
Read about them in the book of Leviticus. When we do not realise the origin of Easter as Passover, and Pentecost as Weeks, and ignore Trumpets, Tabernacles and the Day of Atonement, it is little wonder that we lose our blessing.

In Malachi, the last book of the Old Testament, 3:10 God rebukes us.
"*You rob me,*" says the Lord God, "*in tithes and offerings. You are under a curse – the whole nation of you – because you are robbing me. Bring the whole tithe into the storehouse, and see if I will not throw open the floodgates of heaven and pour out so much blessing that you will not have room enough for it! Test me in this!*"

And every time we do give for the work of the Gospel, we find we are blessed many times over. God is a God of multiplication, not addition. Remember the two fishes and the five loaves that Jesus blessed, which fed five thousand men and their families with twelve baskets to spare!

Jesus confirms this in Luke 6:38
He says "Give, and it will be given unto you. A good measure, pressed down, shaken together and running over, will be poured into your lap. For with the measure you use, it will be measured to you.

"Test me in this," says God, in Malachi, *"and see the mighty blessings that are I will pour into you!"* As George Verwer, who has a ministry of giving out free Christian books from his ships travelling all over the world said to me "You can never outgive God!"

And when we have read and obeyed the Word, tithed and made extra offerings following the Judaic law that Jesus himself followed, and practised complete forgiveness to everyone, healing comes.
"They will be mine, says the Lord God, in the day when I make up my treasured possession. For you who revere my name, the sun of righteousness will arise with healing in its wings. Malachi 4:2

The church may ask "Why do the faithful get sick?" Sometimes sickness has come in the form of a generational curse, through sin of our ancestors – *"because of the sin of their fathers"* Leviticus 26:40. We have to repent of any sins on behalf of our forefathers, and the curse rebuked through the cleansing blood of Jesus, so that healing can take place. We know how an unfaithful father can produce an unfaithful son, and an impatient mother produce an impatient daughter. But when Jesus comes into our lives, we can see the whole picture, and heal.

Sickness may also be caused by an attack of the enemy on an individual who is doing an excellent job serving the Lord, and the devil is trying to kill that person. Remember the threat is very real;

Jesus said *"the devil comes to steal, kill and destroy"* John 10:10. but Jesus *"comes to bring us life in all abundance."*

Ephesians 6:10 tells us to wear the full armour of God and to pray at all times. We must wear the belt of truth, the breastplate of righteousness, the shoes of peace, the shield of faith, the helmet of salvation and the Sword of the Spirit which is the Word of God.

The devil can always be overcome by praying in the Spirit, by rebuke and exorcism, and by claiming the blood of Jesus. Jesus won our salvation with the front of the cross, but he also won our healing with the back of the cross, as his back was ripped open to the bone by the lashes he received. *"By His stripes we are healed"* prophesied Isaiah in chapter 53 of his book, hundreds of years before Jesus lived. Believe, and the victory has been won!

James 5:14 says we should *"call the elders of the church to pray over us and anoint us with oil in the name of the Lord. And the prayer offered in faith will make the sick person well; the Lord will raise him up. If he has sinned, he will be forgiven. Therefore confess your sins to each other and pray for each other so that you may be healed. The prayer of a righteous man is powerful and effective.* Dying to self often brings the healing!

Sometimes the sin is that the sick person has insulted the Holy Spirit. Jesus says that this is the one unforgivable sin. We must remember that the Lord is a jealous God, he will not abide us loving anyone or anything more than him. Even our husband, wife and children have to take second place. And that is the salvation of a home, because when husband, wife and children love the Lord first, they will love each other even better than any secular family could. Every marriage should have Jesus at its heart. *Psalm 127:1 says "Unless the Lord build the house, its builders labour in vain."*

In the Song of Solomon 2:15 it is *"the little foxes that spoil the vine".* They are the little problems which can disturb or destroy a relationship. These irritations must not be minimised or ignored. They must be identified so that, together, in prayer to the Father, Christians can deal with them. It is the presence of the Holy Spirit in such discussions that can solve them, and the Holy Spirit alone.

If you really want healing, return to the Lord and He will return to you. Jesus says in John 14:15 "if you really love me you will keep my commandments." When we do, we will be completely healthy, joyful and at peace. God has an incredible future and destiny for all of us when we are obedient to his Word.

Sickness is an opportunity for God to show His strength. An American woman called Joni Eareckson Tada has a huge speaking ministry. Completely paralysed from the neck down from a diving accident when she was a teenager, this courageous, faithful woman testifies from her wheel chair. Our weakness is made perfect in His strength. She wipes away the surface grit of suffering and circumstances to reveal the radiant hope that each of us can claim through Jesus. Joni says that she knows God will restore her in a different, heavenly body.

For people like Joni who are awaiting their healing and are assured of their salvation, Paul has words of encouragement in Philippians 4:12 and 13. Paul had suffered greatly for the Gospel, has been savagely beaten, stoned, incarcerated, and shipwrecked. From prison, in chains, he writes:

"I have learned the secret of being content in any and every situation, whether well fed or hungry, whether living in plenty or in want, I can do everything through Him who gives me strength".

There is nothing like healing to bring people to believe in God, as happens through the Holy Spirit. These healings can happen spontaneously during praise, when preachers like Greek Benny Hinn, born in Jaffa in the Holy Land, hold crusades, preaching the blood and the cross, around the world.

I have assisted in five international crusades held by Benny Hinn and have seen people next to me healed dramatically, and seen that after years, they have kept their healing. It is genuine and it is the Holy Spirit who is healing, as He did in the book of Acts.

The healings are granted by the mercy of God in these last days to bring people to belief. Orthodox Jews, Catholics, Muslims, Hindus and Sikhs all fall in the Holy Spirit and are healed. Then they come to faith, their greatest healing.

As the prophet Joel says 2:28
"I will our pour out my Spirit on all people
Your sons and daughters will prophesy,
Your old men will dream dreams,
Your young men will see visions.
Even on my servants, both men and women,
I will pour out my Spirit in those days."

Jesus said he will return, but *"no one knows the hour of his coming."* However, most Spirit filled believers feel that the signs are already on the fig tree, and the Lord will be coming back soon. Healing is coming to the church in this time of favour, so that many might believe.

We are body, mind and spirit, just as God is body (Jesus) mind (the Father) and spirit (the Holy Spirit). When we are perfectly aligned with God's Word in the Old and New Testaments, we find our perfect healing. Our diet needs to be the Genesis Diet, which God directed us to eat when he created us. Cutting edge research proves this to be the healing diet. It would be, wouldn't it!

I pray that this book will bring about immense healings. It encapsulates the directives given by God to His People with constant reference to biblical text. It stresses that we need to be obedient to God in the natural, in the way we treat our body which is the temple of the Holy Spirit on earth.

We need the Breath of Life, Living Water, Living food and a covering, physically, just as much as we need them spiritually. The church has omitted to teach healing and the blessing since 325AD. No wonder Christians have become ill.

We need revival physically as well as spiritually. It takes courage and determination to follow God's plan for us. We need to break out of the conventions and compromise of the world! The story of the robin and the caterpillar illustrates this:

The robin says to the caterpillar;
"Oh, do come on,
come out of that gloomy dark ditch and feel the sun and blue skies."

The caterpillar replies "I'm quite cosy here, thank you, dear.
I'm used to this ditch.
My friends live here, we all shelter together in the dark."

The robin continues;
"But it's such a joy to be free of the dark! To fly in the blue skies, to sit in the high branches of the ash tree, and to feel the warmth of the sun on my wings!"

The caterpillar says "I suppose it is, dear, but I haven't got the energy to move."
She thinks ... "Wings ..... wings ....." But she does nothing.

The caterpillar gets slower and colder
and grows a shell round her.
She becomes so still and silent and hard
that everyone in the ditch thinks she has died.
They miss her, she had been a quiet, inoffensive little caterpillar.

At last the sun/Son breaks through,
and a gorgeous scarlet butterfly lands on a bluebell
above the caterpillar.
"Its time to break out of your cocoon."

It's the hardest struggle the caterpillar has ever had,
breaking out of the hard shell of the chrysalis.
She struggles and struggles to get rid of her shell.
But she eventually breaks through.
She sees her reflection in a puddle. She is reborn. She is absolutely beautiful!

"I see your wings are still folded", says the butterfly,
"but I will wait beside you until they fully open and dry,
and you are ready to fly.
The rest of us are waiting for you in the rose garden."

I hope to meet you one day in God's garden.

When you have been healed, pass God's Word on to others. Make your test into a testimony! Sow the seed and reap the harvest! Every church needs a healing ministry, led by people who have been healed themselves.

As St. Paul says in 2 Corinthians 1:3-5
"Praise be to the God and Father of our Lord Jesus Christ the Father of compassion and the Lord of all comfort, who comforts us in all our troubles, so that we can comfort those in any trouble with the comfort we ourselves have received from God."

Be blessed, be healed, and be a witness to God's Healing Word!

A FEW GOOD IDEAS TO EXPERIMENT WITH!

RAW AND LIGHTLY COOKED RECIPES

(If we eat 80% raw living enzymes, we can have 20% lightly cooked food!)

Some Ideas for Breakfasts

Green Barley Juice
Always start your day with this wonderful de-toxifier! The tender shoots of young green barley have been scientifically proven to be the purest source of green vegetables, grown high in the mountains above any pollution. Slip the blade of a knife into the powder and gently lift the barley grass powder into a bottle of distilled water, secure the cap and shake to reconstitute. Pour into a glass and drink this Green Barley Juice before other juices. An acquired taste, but well worth persevering! Chase it down with….

Carrot and Apple Juice freshly juiced
Always make this the basis of your other juices because carrot and apple are SO nutritious! You can add some mango, or pineapple, or strawberries or peaches or any other fresh seasonal fruits to vary the flavour.

Hot Honey, Lemon and Ginger Drink
Infuse some finely chopped fresh root ginger in boiling distilled water. Allow to simmer gently for ten minutes while you make the other juices. Sieve into a breakfast cup and add one teaspoon each of raw runny honey and fresh lemon juice.

Banana and Almond Smoothie
Blend a banana, a little lemon juice, a teaspoon of raw runny honey and a dessertspoon of flaked almonds with distilled water until smooth.

Home made Museli
Mix together a teaspoon of flaked almonds, linseeds, sesame seeds, pine nuts, pumpkin seeds, sunflower seeds, raisins, chopped figs, cherries, coconut, and organic dates. Juice two apples and pour the juice over the muesli.

Seeded biscuits with honey
Dr. Karg biscuits with a variety of good seeds. Top with natural honey.

Lunches and Suppers

Avocado Soup
Blend the avocado with fresh home made vegetable stock, a little lemon juice and natural organic yoghurt. Garnish with a swirl of the yoghurt.

Avocado Dressing
Slice the avocados in half, and scoop the flesh out into a blender with a spoon.
Add a squeeze of lemon juice to stop the avocado flesh oxidising and turning brown.
Add a little chopped onion and blend until smooth.

Baked Potato
(do not eat potatoes and tomatoes if you have an allergy to the deadly nightshade vegetables)
Pour some olive oil and salt on a large potato.
Wrap in grease proof paper and bake for an hour until soft.
Cut a cross into the top, pinch to open, and fill with parsley butter or avocado dressing and serve with a crisp green salad.

Cauliflower Soup
Sauteé two chopped onions and two medium sized par boiled potatoes in a deep saucepan with virgin olive oil. Add cauliflower florets, basil and a little Celtic sea salt. When softened, add organic vegetable stock. Blend with a stick blender in the saucepan and serve in heated soup bowls. Garnish with ground almonds which have been sautéed for one minute in pure butter.

Coleslaw
Shred cabbage, red and yellow peppers and an onion in a food processor.
Mix the vegetables in a bowl with a dressing of runny honey, Celtic sea salt, lemon juice and extra virgin olive oil.

Courgette and Tomato Bake
Thinly slice onions, garlic, courgettes and tomatoes.
Layer the vegetables in a lightly oiled baking dish.
Cover with a thin layer of mustard and bake in 150 degree oven for half an hour.

Cucumber Soup
Peel and seed three large cucumbers, chop a stalk of celery and a red onion.
Peel two courgettes. Blend all ingredients, add distilled water to get right consistency and top with chives.

Curried green lentil soup
Chop an onion and three cloves of garlic and sautée them gently in olive oil.
Add a dessertspoon of curry powder and stir.
Rinse a cupful of green lentils and add to the mixture.
Add half a litre of organic vegetable stock
Simmer the soup for around half an hour, until soft
Whiz with a stick blender, add a little lemon juice and salt, and serve with a swirl of yoghurt on top.

Essene Bread
(if you yearn for bread, this is the best!
No yeast, no refined flour, no sugar or salt)
A quarter of a cup of almonds soaked overnight and drained
A quarter of a cup of walnuts soaked overnight and drained
3 pitted dates soaked in a separate bowl until soft, (about one hour) and drained.
Half an apple peeled and shredded
1 clove of garlic, minced
1 teaspoon of fresh chopped parsley
2 tablespoons of extra virgin olive oil
Two cups of sprouted spelt

Put the sprouted spelt and dates into the food processor along with the remaining ingredients and process until a dough consistency is reached. Bake at 150 degrees for 45 minutes or until the bread is crisp on the outside and moist on the inside.

Gazpacho
(Reserve a small amount of each raw chopped vegetable as you add them to this recipe, for decoration)
Blend two large tomatoes with a quarter of a cup of vegetable stock until smooth.
Place in a bowl.
Add two cups of peeled and diced cucumbers, two stalks of diced celery, half a seeded and diced green pepper, one whole seeded and diced red pepper, and three sliced onions.
Stir in 2 tablespoons of extra virgin olive oil, two tablespoons of lemon juice, a little Celtic Sea salt. Cover and chill. Garnish with reserved chopped vegetables.

Guacamole
Cut two ripe avocado pears in half, scoop out the flesh and reserve the shells.
Put the flesh in a bowl and add the juice of one clove of garlic, a dash of Tabasco sauce, lemon juice or fresh lime juice, one dessertspoon of olive oil, one sliced onion, one sliced tomato, half a red pepper, one stalk of celery and blend in a processor.
Spoon the mixture back into the reserved shells.

Honeyed carrots
Choose baby carrots, or slice larger ones
Simmer the carrots gently in distilled water to soften, adding a little Celtic sea salt.
Drain, and drizzle with honey mixed with melted butter.

Honeyed Carrot, Almond, Walnut and Coriander Soup
Heat three tablespoons of butter and three tablespoons of olive oil very gently in a large saucepan, until the butter has melted.
Add two chopped onions and cook for five minutes, add the chopped leek and chopped carrots and cook over a gentle heat for 5 minutes.
Stir in the honey, lemon juice and coriander and cook, stirring for 2-3 minutes.

Add home made vegetable stock and a handful of ground almonds. Bring to the boil, stirring. Reduce heat, cover and simmer for 20 minutes.
Remove from heat, cool the mixture, then blend until smooth.
Season with Celtic sea salt and a little freshly ground black pepper.
Reheat gently and serve immediately sprinkled with walnuts and garnished with coriander.

Amanda's Hummus
Soak chickpeas overnight.
Rinse and boil for 40 minutes the next day.
Put them in the food processor
Add the juice of lemon and the juice of three cloves of garlic.
Add two heaped dessertspoons of Tahini paste
Drizzle a little olive oil into the mixture until it is the right consistency.
Add cumin, coriander powder to taste, a little freshly ground black pepper and a pinch of Celtic sea salt.
Blend for 10 minutes until creamy

Jersey New Potatoes
Simmer some new baby Jersey potatoes gently in their skins with chopped mint for ten minutes.
Drain, serve on a hot dish and drizzle with melted butter.

Raw Carrot, Almond and Parsley Soup
Blend two cups of home made vegetable stock with half a cup of chopped almonds, a cup of fresh parsley and half a teaspoon of Celtic Sea salt. Add six chopped carrots and blend until smooth.
Pour into bowls, garnish with chives.

Ratatouille
Soften two chopped red onions, two cloves of garlic, two chopped aubergines, three chopped red peppers, one kilo of skinned, sliced tomatoes and four chopped courgettes in nine tablespoons of virgin olive oil and four ml of water.
Add a little chopped oregano, marjoram, parsley, sea salt and freshly ground black pepper.
Simmer, stirring from time to time, for one hour.

Add another six tablespoons of olive oil after an hour and check the seasoning.

Rice with onions, garlic and flaked almonds
(Bernard's Special Rice)
This recipe serves two.
Peel and chop a medium onion
Put three table spoonfuls of olive oil in non stick saucepan.
Add the onions and cook at medium heat until onions are soft and translucent.
Add half a mug of long grain rice and one and a quarter mugs of distilled water.
Bring to the boil briefly, then cook afterwards on medium heat until nearly all the water has gone.
Turn off the heat, put a lid on saucepan and leave the rice to absorb the rest of the water for fifteen minutes. Add chopped parsley. Mix thoroughly and serve.

Salad dressing
Whisk runny honey, virgin olive oil, mustard and a dash of lemon juice. Pour over the salad immediately while the ingredients are well mixed.

Salsa dressing
Blend three skinned tomatoes, a red pepper, a stick of celery, basil, oregano, a pinch of Celtic sea salt, a sliced onion, cucumber, extra virgin olive oil, garlic and honey.

Spiced Red Cabbage
Melt 50 grams of butter and one tablespoon of olive oil in a saucepan over a medium heat. Add one small red cabbage, finely sliced. Add one red onion, finely sliced.
Add 50 ml balsamic vinegar, half a teaspoon of allspice, two tablespoons of honey,
half a teaspoon of ground cloves, Celtic sea salt, freshly ground black pepper and 200 ml of water. Bring to the boil, reduce the heat, cover and simmer for an hour, checking frequently. Add more water if the cabbage gets too dry.

Steamed spinach
Tear the spinach leaves, removing any stalks.
Steam lightly and add some butter.

Stir fried vegetables
Chose fresh organic vegetables, chop and slice,
Sauté in olive oil briefly to soften in a wok,
Add a little soy sauce for flavour.

Stuffed tomatoes
Cut a large ripe tomato in half.
Blend slices of onion, flaked almonds, pine nuts, chopped garlic, celery and parsley.
Spoon on top of the tomato halves.
Drizzle with virgin olive oil.
Bake in the oven on 100 degrees for ten minutes.

Tahini paste
Blend one cup of sesame seeds and two garlic cloves to create nut butter.
Add lemon juice, Celtic sea salt, water, and blend again until you have the right consistency.

Tomato and Onion soup
Chop three onions and simmer in a heavy saucepan with olive oil until they are soft.
Add three chopped organic tomatoes, a little Celtic sea salt and basil.
Add distilled water to correct consistency.
When lightly cooked, blend and garnish with parsley.

Tomato, Avocado, Onion and Carrot Soup (cold)
Peel three cups of fresh tomatoes and a ripe avocado, and blend until smooth.
Chop one small onion, and one stalk of celery.
Add one teaspoon of oregano and one of basil, one tablespoon of lemon juice and a little Celtic Sea Salt. Blend, stir in some carrot juice before serving.

Vegetable Curry

Chop two onions and three cloves of garlic. Sauté them in butter or olive oil for five minutes. Stir in a teaspoon of curry paste. Add two chopped and peeled apples, omitting the core but adding the precious pips, full of B17. Add a handful of raisins, a chopped carrot, a chopped pepper, a chopped courgette, and four spears of broccoli, a handful of French beans, peas, two tomatoes, and a little lemon juice.

Add chick peas or kidney beans to make the curry more substantial. Simmer until lightly cooked. Serve with natural brown basmati rice, chutney and organic natural yoghurt.

Warldorf Salad

Chop two sticks of celery, add two peeled and chopped apples and a handful of fresh walnuts. Serve with honey, mustard, olive oil and lemon juice dressing.

Your Just Desserts

Almond, honey and raisin bar

Mix crushed almonds, a little sesame nut butter, honey and raisins together.

Press into a tin which has been lightly oiled with olive oiled and set in the fridge. When set, cut into bars.

Apple purée

Peel, slice and gently simmer apples until they are soft, blend until smooth with a little lemon juice and honey.

Baked apple

Scrub some organic cooking apples, and scoop out the core. Reserve the precious pips which contain vitamin B17.

Fill the empty centre with raisins and honey.

Place in a baking tin with a little water which reaches a quarter way up the apple. Bake for half an hour on 150 degrees until the apple flesh is soft. Remove from oven, drizzle with more honey and the apple pips.

Banana Cream
Blend two bananas, juice of half a lemon, honey and Greek Yoghurt. Pour into tall wine glasses and decorate with flaked almonds.

Banana Smoothie
Blend two bananas with fresh organic berries and one or two stoned organic dates, together with a little honey and one cup of fresh apple juice. Top with a few reserved berries and flaked almonds.

Figs
Peel ripe figs and serve with a thick sauce of honey and a little distilled hot water.

Fruit Salads
Wash and prepare seasonal organic grapes (with seeds!), stoned dates, sliced apples, peeled and sliced oranges, strawberries, raspberries, red currants, blackberries, pineapple chunks, stoned cherries, sliced figs, tangerines or satsumas, sliced mango, peach, melon and payaya.

Peach Smoothie
Juice one apple, and two ripe, stoned peaches,
Blend this juice with a little distilled water and two bananas and a dessertspoon of honey.

Strawberry Smoothie
Blend a handful of flaked almonds with fresh strawberries (or raspberries or blueberries) and a little distilled water to the desired consistency.

Summer fruit and Honey Smoothie
Blend a cup of apple juice, a tablespoon of honey, half a cup of Greek yoghurt with two cups of frozen summer fruits (raspberries, strawberries, blackcurrants).
Serve decorated with extra summer fruits.

Revivers to have mid morning or at "tea" time

Because it is better for the body to have several nourishing small meals rather than just three large ones, I hope you will enjoy these "revivers". Remember you never need to be hungry on the Genesis Diet, you just learn to snack on nutritious things.

Hot Honey, Lemon and Ginger drink made with distilled water, decorated with mint.
Fruit – you can snack on grapes instead of chocolate!
You can always have an apple.
You can always have fresh juices.
You can always have carrot and apple juice and other vegetable juices.
You can always have hot vegetable soups.
Smoothies - Strawberries and almond smoothie
Sesame and almond bars with fruit and honey
Greek yoghurt blended with fresh raspberries, strawberries, peaches, pineapple or kiwi fruit.

If you want to lose weight, do not eat after seven in the evening. Keep to the Genesis diet, drink plenty of distilled water and take exercise!

Thanks

My loving thanks, above all, to God
who has blessed me with healing
and
given me the health and direction
to write this book.

My thanks and admiration also
to the children of God,
the "flowers of the field",
who work as pastors,
Bible believing doctors, biochemists and researchers
and who have revealed to me
natural cures
based on the Word of God.

Very special thanks
to my family
and my larger church family around the world
who pray for me so faithfully.

In the years since Melanie went to be with the Lord,
I have gleaned like Ruth,
amid the alien corn throughout the world,
from every source which I felt through the Holy Spirit
to be of God,
which has become this book....

"God's Healing Word"

Felicity
Easter 2006
Jersey, Channel Islands, Jerusalem and Portugal